WARM WINTER
LOVE

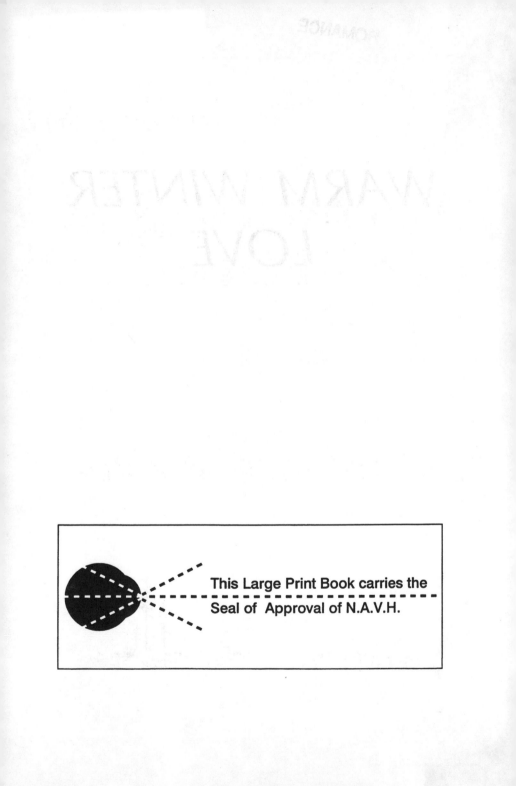

WARM WINTER LOVE

Constance Walker

Thorndike Press • Thorndike, Maine

Library of Congress Cataloging in Publication Data:

Walker, Constance.
   Warm winter love / Constance Walker.
      p.   cm.
   ISBN 1-56054-601-8 (alk. paper : lg. print)
   1. Large type books.   I. Title.
[PS3573.A425324W37   1993]   92-37973
813'.54—dc20   CIP

Thorndike Large Print® Candlelight Series edition published in 1993 by arrangement with Avalon Books.

Cover photo by Tom Knobloch.

The tree indicium is a trademark of Thorndike Press.

This book is printed on acid-free, high opacity paper. ∞

To Ben, with love.
Here's still looking at you, kid!

Chapter One

The students weren't the only ones who needed a vacation. After four solid months of work, the teachers at Southern High were feeling the pressure of instructing pupils who would sometimes have preferred to be outside in the cold winter air. Increasingly, Katie Jarvis had had to abandon her class and go out to intimidate students who had decided that lunch hour or study hall had come early. She would be standing in her classroom, trying to teach the difference between poetry and prose, and she would look out the window and see the kids huddled together on the football field. Leaving her class, she would march out coat-less in the cold weather and herd the errant students back into their classroom.

That Wednesday, in the week before winter break, after the last bell, Katie sat down at her desk with packets of travel folders among the English lit books and stacks of students' essays. She hunched over the desk, her chin resting on her hands, her eyes on the four-color brochures parading the snow and slopes of Pennsylvania, and she took a deep breath. *Three more days,* she said to herself. *Three more days and I'll be there.* She closed her eyes, lost in the reverie of seven days of skiing, seven days without books and poems. *No, erase that thought.* She was going to take along her favorite poetry books so that she could just sit and immerse herself in the haunting poems of Coleridge and Frost without the school bell of her mind reminding her to prepare lesson plans. . . .

It was going to be wonderful. Too bad no one was going with her. Poor Jason! If only he would try skiing. Just once. Just once even going up the beginning slopes or on a trail across a snow-covered field. He'd know immediately what fun it could be. But Jason was insistent — no skiing, no snow, no cold weather. "I have enough here," he would say whenever Katie brought up the subject for his consideration. "No, Katie, you go by yourself. It's your vacation. I might as well get used to it. When we marry, I can't expect you to stop skiing. You enjoy it so much. I'll just stay here." He would pick up her hand, stroke it, and smile, and Katie would know that that was the end of the conversation. So be it!

"Are you dreaming of skis, straps, boots, and all the other paraphernalia?" Rene, Katie's best friend and Southern High's algebra teacher, said as she came through the door.

8

Katie started putting everything into her briefcase. "I wish you'd come with me."

"No way, Katie. I'm heading for warmer climates this time around. That's the only thing your Jason and I have in common. The hotter the sun, the better."

They were almost the last ones to leave the school, and as they walked through the deserted halls, Katie mused silently about her own years here as a student.

"They've changed," she said to Rene.

"Who?" Rene pushed open the door.

"The kids. They're so . . . so practical now, so different from us when we were their age."

"And you?" Rene looked at her friend. "Haven't you changed too? It's the times."

"I guess so." Katie got into her car. "Jason and I are going out to dinner this evening. Want to join us?"

Rene shook her head. "Thanks, but no thanks. I've got a stack of papers that have to be graded." Rene looked up at the school building. "Oh, Katie, sometimes don't you wish we were still students without a care in the world? Without having to make any other decision than what to wear to school or how hard to study for a test?"

Katie smiled but didn't answer. She backed her car out of its parking space and eased carefully onto the road. She glanced into the rearview mirror to make sure that she was keeping up with traffic. Seeing her reflection, she pushed back the dark hair that had fallen across her brow. Another glance in the mirror told her that she was now the only one on the road, and after a critical glance at herself, she rubbed her pale cheeks to redden them. She came to a stoplight, and while waiting for the green, she reached into her handbag, pulled out a tube of lipstick, and freshened her lips without taking her eyes off the road. Then another quick glance into the mirror just as the green light appeared. There — at least she wouldn't look so washed out . . . so plain.

Not that Jason would mind, or even notice. No, he wasn't the kind of guy who cared about externals. That's why she was first attracted to him. Jason was solid, the type of man every mother wanted her daughter to marry, and even though her mother no longer lived in Maryland, Katie was sure that her mother would approve of Jason. After all, what was there not to like about him? Yes, Katie assured herself, she was a lucky woman. She had a good job, good friends, and she was engaged to Jason.

She pulled into the driveway of her apartment house and parked her car, glancing once more into her rearview mirror. Yes, ma'am, she was a lucky person. She had everything she had ever dreamed of when she was younger. Absolutely everything.

As she rode the elevator to her floor, she skimmed through her mail. There were no real letters, just advertisements from companies wanting her to buy stocks and bonds and all sorts of merchandise. Somehow she had gotten on their lists and now she was being bombarded.

In her kitchen area she opened the refrigerator, reached for a cookie, and then put it back. Jason would be over soon and this would only spoil her dinner. She quickly closed the refrigerator and crossed over to the couch, pulling the stack of ungraded essays next to her. *Might as well start these,* she thought, already beginning to underline spelling mistakes.

Jason arrived on the dot of seven, just as he did every Wednesday. They would go to The Country Cottage for their usual soup and salad, spend an hour and a half eating and talking, and then he would take her home. There she would make coffee and they would trade stories about their students. Jason was a science teacher and part-time baseball coach. Somewhere around ten-thirty he would go home after giving her a very brief kiss. All was perfectly safe and all had been perfectly repeated for the last five months.

"Jason, do you sometimes want things to be different? To change?" She toyed with her salad, pushing the green olives around her plate, not looking at him.

"No, I never thought about that. I'm happy with the way things are, aren't you?" Jason had a habit of always answering a question with a question.

She bit into an olive. "Yes, but sometimes I just get . . . oh, I don't know. I just get a little. . . ."

"What you need is that vacation, Katie. We're all on edge. You'll see, when you get back you'll be ready to go again." He pointed his fork at her. "Take my word for it — we all need the time off."

"I suppose." She watched as Jason paid the bill. "I wish you would let me pay my half."

"Some other time." He put his billfold into his pocket.

"You always say that."

He smiled and put his hand on her shoulder and guided her out of the restaurant.

Katie studied Jason's profile as they drove home in the dark. He was really rather handsome, she thought. Certainly the women teachers at school thought so, and she knew that the waitresses at The Country Cottage thought so too, judging by the way they always fussed over him. Of course they were a bit older than he, but even the girls in his class flirted with him. That was an occupational hazard, he had said when she teased him about it. Almost all high-school students had a crush on some teacher at one time or another, or so he had read. Still, it was nice to know that other people liked your choice of the man you were going to marry.

There was something in the set of Jason's mouth — she could see it even now as light filtered into the car from passing streetlights — a certain something that projected a strong character, that told her that no matter what was going to happen, Jason would always be there for her. It was something she didn't even have to think about, let alone discuss. She just knew that Jason would always be faithful, that there would be no other women in his life . . . ever. And he would always be home in the evenings with her, not like her father, who had always been somewhere up or down the East Coast throughout the week, selling machinery to the shipyards, sometimes not making it home for even part of the weekend. No, that was another plus for Jason — he would always be there, and she would always be able to count on him. On birthdays, holidays, and summer vacations, Jason would be with her.

"Why so quiet?" He turned up the heater.

"Oh, I don't know . . . just thinking."

"About us?" He smiled and she nodded.

"Yes, just thinking about how nice it is being with you." She leaned her head on his shoulder. "How nice it is with you now and how it will be later when. . . ." She shrugged. "I just feel very comfortable with you, Jason," she added, and he softly squeezed her hand.

Later, after their coffee and after Jason had left, while she was grading the last of the papers, she remembered Rene's words: "Haven't you changed too?" She put down the blue marking pencil and rubbed her nose.

Have I? she asked herself. She leaned back against the cushions of the couch and looked around the living room and at her collection of music boxes on the end table. She leaned over and picked one up, listening to the faint, tinny sound of an almost unrecognizable tune. "Maybe I have," she said, replacing it on the table. "Maybe I have."

Chapter Two

In her room at the lodge, Katie looked out her window at the mountains dotted with skiers in brightly colored jackets and hats —and she smiled. This was what she had waited for, what she needed. Jason was right, they were all a bit tired of the school routine. This vacation would give her some respite, and then she'd be ready to return to teaching poetry.

She looked around and saw the deep piles of snow, and heard, even through the glass, the sounds of delighted children playing on their skis, taking their first runs on the beginners' slopes. Yes, this was what she needed, this was her kind of weather, her kind of vacation. No matter what Jason and Rene said, nothing could compare to this scene. Forget about the sun and the water and the beach. Why would anyone prefer sand when he could have this?

She opened the window and took a deep breath of the cold air into her lungs, and then shivered. This had always been her one vice — a week's vacation in the mountains in the winter. How lucky she was that Jason understood her, that he encouraged her to get away.

She unpacked his picture from her suitcase — the picture of the two of them in front of the school, he with his arm around her shoulders, and she laughing at something someone had said. She polished the glass. *Dear Jason, good old Jason,* she thought, and then she set the frame on her bureau. If he chose not to come with her — well, at least he could be here in the photo.

It was a dazzling white outside, the bright sunshine reflected in the endless blanket of snow that covered the entire skiing area. Real snow — not man-made — with more predicted to fall this evening and tomorrow. She put on her cap, slung her skis over her shoulder, and headed for the slopes. It was now time for fun, she thought, and laughed.

There weren't more than ten people waiting in line for the lift to Magic Mountain, the medium slope, and while Katie tightened her ski straps, she looked toward the top of the mountain, adjusting her eyes to the blur of the stark whiteness. She pulled down her sunglasses and reached for the T-bar, thinking as it whisked her up the mountain that she had already forgotten about assignments and book reports and everything else about teaching. Already the winter sport had pushed out all the other thoughts in her mind.

She took her first run slowly, wanting to

savor the experience, wanting to take in the full enjoyment of the downhill slide. By the time she had gone up and skied down the third time, she was back to her old form.

"Nice run."

She heard the deep voice behind her, and she turned and saw a tall, slim man in a red nylon parka. "Nice," he said, motioning toward the run, and she realized that he was speaking to her.

"Thanks. I've been waiting for two months just to get here." She took hold of the T-bar again, and she saw that the man was in back of her, next in line. When she reached the top once more, she felt that she had to say something. "Fantastic day, isn't it?" There, that was a nice, innocent statement. "You have to be careful," she remembered Jason's cautioning her. Too many times her friendliness had been misinterpreted.

The stranger smiled at her. "Yes, just the right temperature for skiing," he said, and then motioned her to go down ahead of him. "You were here first."

She got into position, nodded, and pushed off.

She made two more passes before noon, and then, exhausted, she went back to her room to take a warm shower and have a rest. No use overdoing it the first day. She had six more glorious days of skiing ahead of her. And if the weather held, she'd take a few more runs in the evening when they lit the slopes. This afternoon, though, she would take a break and go to the little souvenir shop down the road. She wanted to send cards to Jason and Rene and maybe buy something for them.

The shop never seemed to change in all the years that Katie had been coming here. It still smelled of cedar incense and perfumed soaps and potpourri, and at each turn of an aisle, she would pause and inspect the items displayed on the wooden shelves. There were so many things, but nothing seemed right for Jason until she discovered the plastic water globe with the small baseball floating inside. She picked up the ornament and turned it upside down so that the ball bobbed and weaved within the liquid. She grinned. This was absolutely perfect for Jason.

"Hello. So we meet again!" She recognized the voice, and she looked up and saw the skier she had met on the slopes that morning. She smiled at him.

"I see you've given up already too," he said. She nodded. "Yes, it's my first day."

"And it's best not to push it." As he grinned, she noticed that the little lines etched around his golden brown eyes were extensions of his smile, a warm smile that seemed open and innocent and maybe, just maybe, a bit mischievous.

"You're right," she said.

"For a son or a nephew?" he asked, indicating the baseball globe in her hand.

"Neither. For . . . for a friend."

"Nice." He reached for a small, decorated music box. "What do you think of this?"

"I love it, but then I love any music box." She switched it on and watched as the small lace butterfly atop the box flapped its delicate wings in time to the music. "It's lovely," she said.

He frowned. "Do you think a young girl would like it?"

"Oh, yes." *Probably for his daughter,* she thought.

"Good. Then I'll take it. I never know what to buy her when I'm away on trips."

"Your daughter?"

"No," he said emphatically, "for the most beautiful girl in the world — my niece, my sister's daughter. My all-time favorite-in-the-world-female, although I don't get to see her too much. I always like to send something home to her, though, just to let her know her uncle is alive and well." He laughed. "And my sister gets to know where I am, which beats writing letters. I hate writing letters." He turned to the shopkeeper and handed him

19

the box and his credit card. "Telephones are more my style."

She looked at the man, amazed at how easy it was to learn so much about him in just a few seconds. She liked his openness. It would really be nice if Jason were that natural. She moved to another aisle. She knew he was watching her — she could see him out of the corner of her eye as he lounged against a counter — and she felt uncomfortable and glad when the shopkeeper handed him his package. Now she could go back to selecting a gift for Rene. She already had Jason's present.

"Going back to the lodge?" The man held the door open as he addressed her. "If you are, I'll wait if you want me to, and we can walk back together."

Katie shook her head. "That's not necessary." She smiled at him and explained, "I have to get another present." She picked up a woolen scarf. "But thanks for asking." She meant it. It had been a nice gesture.

"Well, maybe we'll see each other on the slopes." The man held up his package. "Thanks again for the help."

Katie put down the scarf, which really wasn't Rene's style. Maybe this little glass skier ornament would be better. She examined it. Yes, it was definitely Rene. She'd probably put it on her desk at school.

Dinner was being served by the time she got back to the lodge, and after she had washed and changed, she went down to the dining room, hoping for a table by the window so that she could see the mountains. But because of the time, all the window tables were taken, and she was seated at the far end of the room, with a view mostly of the big potted palm near her. Tomorrow she would remember to ask the hostess to reserve her a table. That way she wouldn't be disappointed.

The room was crowded and the fact that she was alone didn't bother her; this was what she wanted and needed — time out for privacy, with no one to ask questions or intrude on her thoughts. *Peace,* she thought. *It's blessed peace. But still.* . . . She looked at the diners at the surrounding tables with a small feeling of envy. Yes, it would be nice to have some company. *Oh, Jason,* she thought, *I'm just going to have to teach you to ski!*

She looked across the room, at and through the windows, and in the twilight she was able to see the hulking shape of the mountain, a huge, shadowy entity that seemed to fade into the night itself. She loved that mountain — it was as though she knew it trail by trail, inch by inch. Magic Mountain was her symbol of nature and reality. She had skied that mountain so many times, enjoying it, allowing the

21

exhilaration of traveling down its side to take over her whole being. Yes, Magic Mountain was her joy!

It was the mountain a few miles away that frightened her. Devil's Mist! She shuddered. Even the name was forbidding. Those trails weren't for her. They looked too frightening . . . too lonely . . . too impossible. Some of the other skiers had told her that the mountain wasn't as menacing or as formidable as it looked. But she didn't believe them. Not even the fact that she was an expert skier could convince her. No, she wasn't about to go down that slope.

Not that she hadn't tried before. She had! When she had first arrived at Mountain Laurel, after conquering Magic Mountain she was ready for more height and speed, and the lodge guides directed her to Devil's Mist, telling her that it was a run for her money. She had picked up her gear and gone there, eager to face the challenge, eager to try the next step. But something happened — she never could quite explain it — and when she stood at the base of Devil's Mist and looked up and saw the low-hung clouds obscuring the top of the run, she panicked. It was such a silly feeling, she had told herself immediately, but nevertheless the feeling remained. It was the beginning of the mental fight whether she, Katie Jarvis, would win and go down the ski run, or whether Devil's Mist would defeat her. So far, Devil's Mist had won.

Katie leaned on her elbow and looked at her mountain, Magic Mountain, as the night lights were being turned on. She thought that it was beckoning to the skiers to come out and play. It was an awesome sight, and she watched so intently that she was startled by the deep voice above her:

"Would you like to join me?"

She looked up and blinked. "I'm sorry. What did you say?" The stranger whom she had now met twice — first on the slopes and then in the shop — smiled at her, and she saw that his teeth were just a little bit uneven, making his smile seem more reckless, as though the rest of the face wanted to laugh a lot and was being held back.

"I asked if you'd like to join me for dinner. I'm sitting over there by the window, third table to the right. I noticed you haven't eaten yet, and neither have I, and I also saw you looking at the mountain. Won't you join me if you're not waiting for anyone."

She looked at his table and the place setting for one. "But my dinner . . . I've. . . ."

"It's all right," he said. "Your waiter will move you." He smiled again. "And I do have a table with a lovely view."

She nodded and stood up. "Yes, I know. And yes, I would like to join you." She motioned toward the mountain. "I can never resist that scene. Thank you." She strolled over to the new table while the stranger spoke to her waiter.

"It's okay," he said to Katie as he joined her. "No trouble at all." He held out his hand to her. "Sam Hubbard."

"I'm Katie Jarvis."

Sam nodded. "And how long have you been a Magic Mountain person?"

"Four years." She sighed. "I found this place by accident and it was love at first sight. What about you?"

"Oh, nothing that long or that romantic, I'm afraid. I'm just your average skier who needed a slope in a hurry, and this was the closest one, according to my travel agent. She promised me lots of snow, good skiing, and good food, which were just what I wanted." He smiled at her again. "But she didn't promise me delightful company. That's a bonus."

Katie turned her head toward the mountain. "Thank you. And what do you think of it?"

"It's not half bad." He broke off a piece of bread and handed the basket to her. "It's not half bad at all. I didn't expect to find skiing this good here."

She buttered her bread. "You've never

24

skied around here before?"

"No." He shook his head. "Out West and in New England, but here in Pennsylvania, no. Maybe I should have come before now." The waiter put steaming bowls of soup in front of them. Sam asked Katie, "Would you care for wine?"

"No, wine's for later. I'm going back out on the slopes this evening, and I want to keep a clear head. Night skiing always disorients me a little. And now that it's almost the end of the season, I don't want to waste one minute."

"Perhaps I'll get out there later too. What do you do, Katie Jarvis? When you're not skiing, I mean?"

"I'm a teacher — English."

"Chaucer and . . .?"

"And all the way through F. Scott Fitzgerald. I do the whole gamut."

He put down his spoon. "I used to be good in that subject. What is that poem — the one that sort of reminds me of this area?"

Katie laughed. "It's got to be Robert Frost's 'Stopping by Woods —"

"— on a Snowy Evening,' " he completed the title. "Yeah, that's it."

"It's still one of the favorite poems I teach. I think everybody knows that one. The kids love it." She sipped her soup, watching as he broke off another piece of bread and buttered it. How easy it was to talk to him. This was the first time she had ever dined with a man here at the lodge, although on the slopes, of course, she had spoken casually to dozens of men. Weather talk or little words of encouragement were always indicated. Skiers were usually a friendly bunch. But as for talking to them away from the trails or runs — well, she never felt comfortable doing that. Everyone always seemed to have his and her own group of friends.

She looked across to Sam. If Rene could see her now! Rene always told her that she should make more friends, be more outgoing. Yes, Rene should see her now. And Jason! What would Jason say?

She looked again at Sam. Yes, what would Jason say? What would he say if she told him that she had had dinner with a rather attractive man? And that she enjoyed it. Jason would probably ask her what she ate. She dipped her spoon into the soup and laughed.

"You're thinking of something funny." Sam tapped the table. "The food? Do you know something I don't?"

"No." She shook her head. "I was just thinking what someone —" She laughed again. "Forget it, Sam. I was just going snow-crazy for a few minutes. First days away from the classroom do that to me."

He shrugged. "During vacationtime you're allowed to go a little crazy."

"I really am, aren't I? Okay, you know that I'm a teacher, but I don't know what you do."

He looked at her quickly. "Guess."

"Twenty questions? This could be fun."

"I'll give you five. After that it gets boring."

"Doesn't it? Okay, you're the president of a bank?"

"One down, four to go." He moved the salt shaker to the side of the table, and she narrowed her eyes at him, trying to envision him in clothes other than the cream-colored sweater and gray slacks he was now wearing.

"You're an artist."

"No. I sketch a little in my spare time, but nothing serious. Three more." He held up three fingers and then moved the pepper mill next to the salt shaker.

"Computers. You work in computers?"

He raised an eyebrow. "I'm impressed. Close. Partly. Go on — what do I do in computers?" His hand toyed with the bud vase.

"I don't know what to say." She gritted her teeth. "You program?"

He moved the flowers to the side. "Two more to go. But I'll give you computers."

She cocked her head to one side. "You sell them."

He returned everything to the middle of the table. "Okay, that's close enough. Remind me I owe you a glass of wine."

"You sell them?"

"The parts, the components."

"Where?"

"All over." He leaned back against his chair. "All over the world."

"You do a lot of traveling?" Katie's voice was low.

"Twenty-five days or more a month." He looked out the window at the snow. "That's why I need something like this every so often. I have to relax. This does it for me." He looked at Katie. "Wherever I am, when I get that 'everything is going haywire' feeling, I just stop, find a place to ski or swim or lie on a beach or whatever, and just relax. Traveling can get to you after a while."

She nodded. "I know." She pushed back her soup bowl. "And now, Sam Hubbard, I'm going back outside." She held out her hand to him and inclined her head toward the window. "Thanks for sharing your view with me."

He half rose. "And thanks for having dinner with me. Maybe I'll see you around . . . or up." He pointed to the mountaintop. "Maybe later." He took her hand and shook it, and she immediately liked the way he grasped it

— strong, meaningful, as though he really meant what he said.

"Yes. Thanks again." She pushed back her chair. "Good-bye, Sam."

"For now, at least."

As he smiled at her once more, she knew that she would meet him again before her vacation was over. It was something she just knew.

Chapter Three

Katie was one of the first skiers on the slopes the next morning, and it was exactly the way she liked it — calm winds, bright sunshine, brittle cold, the kind of weather that ski resorts hope for but rarely get. She loved it when it was like this, when there weren't many people around, when she could feel that she belonged on the mountain, belonged where no one could intrude on her thoughts or even talk to her. These times were far too few; usually, by the time she awoke and got ready, there were long lines of eager, noisy people waiting for the lifts. But today had to be her lucky day — she had gotten to the top of Magic Mountain without any waiting.

She stood at the edge of the run, listening to the wind, letting the snow showers swirl around her, and she blew into the air so that she could see her breath vaporize in front of her. Yes, this was her kind of day. She slapped her hands together and then reached for her poles, ready to shove off.

"Hey, snowbird!"

She turned at the sound of the voice, recognizing the tone and the teasing. "You're up

ss-country trails around here?
't been on, partly because
y and I'm hardly ever in a
vacations. I have enough of
He raised his hand slightly.
Are you game?" He smiled,
there was a gap between his
ll and hardly noticeable, it
him seem so appealing . . .

"Sure. There's a trail across
r miles away, and if we're
e has gotten to it yet." She
oves. "Suppose I meet you
bout an hour."

am was waiting for her, and
from across the room, his
her feel as though she were
the world whom he wanted
as flattered. Sam was good-
esting way. Not really good-
belonged in the movies or
as handsome as Jason. Just
he would be presentable
me to your mother. Katie
down and frowned. Well,
wouldn't approve. Sam was
his ways, and that might
her. Her mother liked her
nified, and Sam was def-

early too!" she said.

Sam was bent over, adjusting the straps on a boot. "Wait until you go down once. It's nearly perfect."

"What time did you get here?" She looked up at the sun. "I thought I'd be one of the first."

"You were," he said, and then laughed. "Only I was *the* first." He moved closer to her. "You know, Katie, I once vowed that I would be number one in something. And this is it." He gave a deep laugh that seemed to enfold her too. He was outrageous. She had never met anyone quite like him, anyone who could laugh and tease so easily. Was he ever serious? She took her place at the top of the run.

"Go on," he said. "I'll go down after you. I want to see how you take some of those curves." He bent down and scooped up some soft snow. "It must have snowed a little last night — all fresh, hardly any tracks in it." He motioned to her. "Go on. I'll see you at the bottom."

Sam was right. The topping of fresh snow gave the trail a better edge, and she kept her eyes straight in front of her, watching as she broke new lines on the surface. This was it, this was close to the feeling that she wanted to experience, a feeling she had waited for.

She had always heard surfers talk about the quest for a perfect wave. Well, this was *her* almost-perfect wave. Someday she would find the perfect run, and then. . . . And then what? Surely it couldn't be any better than this. She glanced up quickly as she shot past a small pine tree, noticing how the branches swayed rhythmically toward and then away from her as her movements stirred the wind. She passed close to another tree, and this time she felt the snow on her face as it fell from the small limbs in the wake of her passing. *Yes, Katie,* she thought, *this is your time.*

"Well, what did you think?" Sam was leaning against a fence. "Worth the trouble of getting up early?"

"Absolutely." She threw back her head and laughed. "Let's do it again."

They made four runs that morning, and when there were too many people ahead of them they took off their skis and went into the coffee shop. She couldn't remember having had so much fun at Mountain Laurel. Too bad Jason wasn't here. He would probably enjoy it even if he only sat in the lounge the whole time and just watched the scenery.

"Hey, Katie-Katie," Sam said, and she smiled at her new name. "What say we go tackle Devil's Mist next?" As he pointed to the mountain a few miles away, she shook her head.

initely not that type. He was too easy, too happy-go-lucky, too full of life. He was a bit like her father. The laugh and the easy manner — that was it. Just like her father as she remembered him from when she was a little girl . . . from before the divorce.

She tossed her head as though she were removing the childhood memories from her mind. That was then and this was now, and Sam wasn't Jason. Sam was just another man who would go on his way come Sunday. She watched as he made his way toward her, and she knew she was smiling. Yes, it was nice to have someone like Sam Hubbard to talk to at Mountain Laurel. He was making the vacation more fun. She might even tell Rene about him.

The cross-country trail led past an old farm, past the neglected, gray, weathered house and barn and sheds. They were all deserted now and the boarded-up house was used only as a marker for skiers who needed landmarks.

They had already passed the farmhouse on their way out, and now, this, their second time in view of the abandoned homestead, on their return to the lodge, they were both delighting in the fact that their trails were the only ones still showing in the snow. They moved closer to each other, trying to ski as near as possible to their original tracks.

At one point Sam made a wrong maneuver and crossed over too early, so that his skis imprinted over her lines for a few feet before he returned to his original position. She pointed to where the tracings merged. "You've double-crossed me, Sam Hubbard," she said, laughing. "You've invaded my territory."

"Would I do that?" he teased. "The best skiing partner I've ever had — would I deliberately cross her up?" Sam pulled back onto his primary course, and with an extra burst of speed he moved ahead of her.

Katie watched the motions of his arms and shoulders and suddenly felt a funny, meltingly warm glow spread throughout her body. She crinkled her eyes as though compressing them would help her to understand what the feeling was, but she couldn't quite sort it out even though the vague, unknown, feathery ticking at her temples seemed to be telling her something . . . to be warning her about something. It seemed strange, but it was as though quite suddenly she knew in this altogether ordinary moment, as she and Sam approached close to the abandoned farmhouse, that everything seemed to be changing for her. It was nothing she could put her finger on . . . nothing so overt that she could say, Yes, that's when she knew it — when she realized that something had happened to the both of them. It was just that strange little feeling . . . a soft, delicate feeling . . . almost as though a puffy cloud had dropped in front of her eyes.

They paused at the porch of the house and sat down on the snow-covered steps, catching their breath and resting for a few minutes before heading back to the lodge. It was late in the afternoon, almost four o'clock, and the sun was beginning to set. The sky was already streaked with a deep rose-pink and blue-gray clouds, and it was at that almost-dusk time of day, when she could see but not really clearly, when she knew that it was time to return to the lodge before night descended quickly and before they would have trouble finding their way back. They began to talk about their lives. She told him about some of her students and the way they acted in her class and even how they called her "Kind-hearted Katie." He laughed and told her he couldn't envision her in a classroom.

It was funny, she thought; she didn't feel reluctant about telling him the stories. She even told him about Rene, her best friend, and how they had both gone to the same school and had grown up together and now were teachers. But, for some reason, she was hesitant to tell him about Jason, and so she avoided speaking about him. He wasn't a topic she wanted to bring up. Besides, there was no reason to tell him about Jason. What would she tell Sam — that she and Jason were engaged . . . that this would probably be her last skiing trip before she married? No, she would keep that to herself. Besides, why would he care?

Sam told her about his childhood in a small town in Arkansas, and how he had gone to a state university and then gotten interested in computers and everything they could do, and how he liked looking at them and taking them apart, and how he had hoped that someday he would own his own computer company. But for now, he said, he was content to be a sales rep and do a lot of overseas traveling, persuading companies to buy his product. It was hard work, but he enjoyed it, enjoyed the challenge.

"I've always had the traveling bug, Katie," he continued. "When I was a kid, if anyone ever said to me, 'Hey, Sam, how would you like to go to . . . ?' — it didn't matter where — whether it was to Rome or London or Chicago or to the corner grocery, I always said sure. Even then I loved to roam. Maybe that's why I like that Robert Frost poem. Maybe someday I'll stop by the woods on a snowy evening or afternoon."

He stretched his legs in front of him so that they dangled on the steps. He looked around him and spread his hands wide. "Maybe someday I'll find another place like this and stop — period! Just stop roaming." He laughed. "But I don't think so, Katie-Katie . . . at least not until I'm old and gray and tired." He dug the tip of his ski pole into the snow and moved it round and round so that it created a small, deep hole. "Did you ever have the wanderlust?" he asked her. "Did you ever want to travel to the ends of the earth?"

She could tell by his tone of voice that he was serious and wanted a serious answer. She shook her head. "No, Sam, this is about as far as I've gone or as far as I want to go except for a few trips to Alabama. That's where my mother lives now, and I go down there to see her occasionally. And I've gone to Canada and Mexico, but that's the extent of my travels. Or my expectations. I suspect I'm a homebody. I like my home, and to have all my friends around me."

He waved toward the lodge. "Katie, you should see Switzerland and the snow and mountains there. And Italy. And all the glories of the winter months in the Alps. You'd love it." He slapped his hands together. "If you like this — the cold and ice and snow and all the things some people think aren't any fun — Well, you just have to see those countries someday."

He took hold of her hands in a gesture of emphasis and she caught her breath. "It's a jumble, Katie, a white-dusted jumble. All kinds of people, all kinds of languages and sounds." He let go of her hands and leaned back against the steps so that the back of his parka was pushed into the accumulated snows. "Someday you have to go there," he said, and for a moment she thought it sounded like a joyous command. "And," he continued, his eyes mischievous and sparkling, "when you get there and you go down the Alps and you want to yell so that the echo keeps bouncing back at you from all sides, remember me, Katie. Remember Sam Hubbard whom you met at Mountain Laurel. Remember that it was he who told you to go there."

He looked at her and laughed and brushed the snow away from his arm. "Someday, Katie Jarvis, when you do get there and you remember me, mark my words that you'll remember that it was on a late afternoon in winter, when it was getting colder and you were getting tired and all you wanted to do was to go back to the lodge, there was this guy who kept talking and talking and he was the one who told you about the Alps and who encouraged you to go there." He scattered some snow from the steps. "Someday you'll remember me and you'll smile. Take my word for it. But do me a favor, because I know you'll be with someone, maybe your husband and maybe even your children — don't tell them about us. Let them always think and conjecture about your mysterious past."

She knew he was teasing, and then they both laughed, but something happened somehow, and his words no longer seemed funny. She stopped laughing, and then she realized that Sam had too.

She put her hand to her face, confused about the strange feeling that was overtaking her again, and she turned to him and saw that he was staring at her, looking at her in a way that made her uncomfortable. She frowned, and they were both quiet, and in the stillness she could hear the call of a blackbird as it passed overhead.

"Katie. . . ." He reached out to her and ran his snow-caked gloves across her cheek slowly. "Katie, I . . ." he said once more, and then before she knew what was happening and before she could control it, he moved his head toward hers and slowly, very slowly, kissed her. When she didn't pull back or protest, he kissed her again.

"Katie," he murmured, and she leaned her head against his shoulder so that she was caught within the circle of his arms. She delighted in the cold nylon of his parka against her face, and for a moment she wanted to yell into the stillness that she wanted to remain in his arms for a long, long time.

He kissed her once more, and it was this last kiss that recalled them both to the present and the lateness of the day. He released her abruptly, letting his hands fall to his sides.

"I don't know what to say, Katie." He stood up and kicked at the snow on the lowest step of the porch. "I. . . ."

She shook her head slightly. "Neither do I." She moved away from him and tugged her hat down tighter over her hair because she didn't know what else to do and she hoped that something physical might break the spell between them. "Maybe," she said slowly and deliberately, "we should just say it was the weather and the fun and the excitement and leave it at that."

"Maybe," he replied, "but then maybe not." He picked up his poles and was quiet for a few moments before he looked at her and finally spoke: "It's getting late, Katie. We'd better go back."

She nodded and moved quickly past him and onto the trail. They were both silent during their return to the lodge. She thought about the episode, refusing to probe why she had responded so easily to him, and she vowed that she wouldn't let anything else happen between her and Sam, that nothing must happen.

She was confused, and all the way back she kept changing her mind about what she would do. At first she thought that she wouldn't see him again, that she would make some excuse not to meet him for dinner anymore and also find an excuse not to ski with him. That would be difficult, she knew, but she could work it so that she would never be in the same area as Sam, not on the mountain or in the lodge or restaurant. But she quickly rejected that idea. She was an adult and could control whatever had happened to them. She certainly could control the situation and see that it didn't happen again.

She kept her head down, looking only as far as necessary in order to find her way back to the lodge. Sam was silent too, and she wondered if he was also questioning the wisdom of the episode. It had happened to them, but what it was she still couldn't admit. She inhaled the cold air as though it would clear her mind so that she could either understand their kiss or forget it completely. But it was too difficult to dismiss. She and Sam had been having such a good time. They had had no worries or cares. And then he had kissed and confused her. She slowly shook her head. No, it hadn't been his fault. Hadn't she leaned her head toward him? Hadn't she offered no resistance? And why talk about fault as though they had done wrong?

"It is wrong," she said aloud. "It never should have happened." That's what she wanted to believe, but she wasn't sure of her reason. She inhaled another breath, gulping it into her lungs as though the icy air would give her the answers. Well, anyway, maybe they'd both forget it and maybe they could both chalk it up to the weather and the time and the circumstance. Yes, that's what it was — just the time and the circumstance. There was no need to ignore him for the next few days. After all, to be fair, she was part and parcel of that moment.

When they met for dinner that evening, neither spoke of the incident, and it was as though it had never happened. Later that night, while lying in bed, she began to believe that the brief romantic moments on the farmhouse steps never really did happen. It was something she had dreamed. At least, she hoped it was only a dream!

Chapter Four

Katie stared out of her window. It was going to be another beautiful day, but somehow the sunshine and the fresh layer of snow really didn't matter right now. She had had a restless night, thinking about Sam, and when she finally fell asleep very late she hadn't resolved anything. She shook her head and wished that she didn't have to think about it, that whatever the problem was, it would just solve itself. She had never had a dilemma like this. She had been having fun. The skiing conditions were near perfect. She was getting lots of rest and relaxation. And everything was exactly what she wanted. But then there was yesterday. And now everything had changed.

"Sam." She said his name softly and then repeated it. He was getting to her, invading her thoughts. He might be a person met only three days ago, but already she was looking forward to seeing and being with him. And that was dangerous. She knew she had no right to be thinking of him, caring about him. Jason was her love. Well, maybe he wasn't her *love*, but he was the man she was engaged to marry. They had an understanding. Right after this

45

semester they were going to begin making plans for their marriage. They had agreed on that; after June they would make all the necessary arrangements for their wedding. Their lives were already charted for the future.

She put her finger to the cold windowpane and traced a snowflake that had fallen against it and melted and was now a drop of water cascading down the glass. All kinds of thoughts and excuses were flooding her mind. Maybe she was fabricating too much out of these days and nights with Sam. Maybe she was just overwhelmed by the wonder of the mountain — her mountain — and that she was at last able to share it with someone . . . with Sam. Perhaps she was making too much of yesterday's kisses. Perhaps it had been just the moment and the closeness. Possibly it would have happened with anyone, anyone who would have teased her and made her laugh, anyone who would have paid her an extra amount of attention. It might be only a momentary fascination. It didn't necessarily mean that she was deeply attracted to Sam. After all, she didn't know anything about him, only that he was a man who traveled a lot, and certainly that wasn't what she wanted. No, that definitely was not what she wanted.

She rubbed at the window. Yes, that was it. She was just caught up with the attention

. . . she was just being swept away because it was so new . . . and because Sam was so different from anyone she had ever met before. She would make a strong effort not to be with him too much today. She'd meet other people, and then everything would be safe. Sam would become just another skier who was at Mountain Laurel for the last snow of the season. He would be someone she had kissed in a moment of exuberance. It really didn't mean a thing. He was probably used to kissing women all around the world. Those kisses probably didn't mean a thing to him. She was just another woman to him, someone he would forget as soon as he got on a jet and left for another trip. And most certainly, he was someone she would forget as soon as she saw Jason again.

She inhaled a deep breath, satisfied with her explanation. She would be okay now. It was funny how a little flattery could go such a long way when you were away from home. Maybe that was why people took vacations, so they could be someone else for a little while. Here at Mountain Laurel she was a woman without ties to the students or the school or even to Jason. There, she had said it again, and she stumbled on the thought. Ties to Jason! Her rationalization wouldn't hold up. She knew that Sam wasn't just another person met on a mountaintop. She was attracted to him — too much so, and she wasn't prepared to do anything about it.

She picked up her scarf. "Katie Jarvis," she said aloud, "you're making much too much out of a three-day meeting with a stranger. Be glad that this is the last cold spell until next year. You'll have come to your senses by then."

Next year . . . next year. The words repeated themselves in her mind. By next year she and Jason would most certainly be married. She swallowed hard when she thought of the word *married*. It was such an absolute word, such a final word. Maybe that wasn't the right attitude for her. That's one other thing she'd have to work on, her lack of enthusiasm. Jason had said that it was merely because she was the kind who never got excited about anything. Well, maybe he was right.

She looked down at the people lined up at the base of the mountain, and she smiled when she spotted a bright red cap like the one Sam had worn the day before. She watched as its bearer walked toward the lodge, and when he got close enough for recognition her smile vanished because it wasn't Sam, just someone who looked like him. No, he didn't look like him at all.

She wondered if Sam was thinking about her, whether he had spent a sleepless night reviewing what had happened. No, he probably was used to flirting and to having women care about him. She turned around and stared at the suitcase next to her bed. If she had any sense she would pack her clothes and go back to Maryland this morning. It was safer there. Safer? What did she mean by safer? Was she afraid of Sam? Or of herself? She was really mixed up. Two days with an attractive man, a man who made her laugh, and see what was quickly happening! She was already acting differently, already beginning to think ridiculous thoughts. *Oh, Katie!* she thought. *You've got four more days. Enjoy them.* That was certainly what Rene would say to her: "Forget about Jason for once. Go out and have some fun."

She smiled. Yes, that's what she would do — she'd go out and have some fun. After all, she was a perfectly sensible and sane schoolteacher on a vacation. She would never change who she was. But still, maybe she should call Jason, just to let him know she was all right and that she was thinking of him. Sure, just hearing his voice would bring her back to her senses. She would call Jason — now!

She placed the call through the lodge operator and let the phone ring five, seven, ten times. He was probably out working with some of his students. Baseball season would be around soon, and he wanted to get a jump on practice time. She replaced the phone, resolving to call him again before dinner. Before she had dinner with Sam.

She picked up her skis. This confusion was surely only something in her mind. Sam wasn't any threat to her or Jason. There was too much history with her and Jason. Sam was an unknown quantity, and she had always stuck to the known.

"Give it up, Katie," she said aloud. "Everything's going to be okay." Glancing at the picture of Jason on the dresser, she said, "Don't worry. After this week you'll be right back where you were with Jason." She tapped the picture and then went downstairs and out of the lodge to the base of the mountain.

"Hi. I wondered where you had gotten to." Sam looked at his watch. "And I thought you were an early bird." He smiled the marvelous smile that made her want to smile too, and she set her skis on the ground. With that smile, who could be afraid of him? And who could believe him? That smile was too easy on his face, too quick, too dazzling. She sighed. His smile was too honest! And too heartbreaking now. But she would escape the charm. She had to!

"Sorry," she said. "I had to make a phone call." She tugged at her boots, not wanting to look at him, not wanting to look deep into his eyes, which seemed to dare her to look deeper into his heart.

"Now?" He waved his hand, indicating the mountain and the line of people waiting for the T-bar. "*Now* you have to call someone? Katie, you really are funny." He bent down to adjust his straps. "You don't call people in the morning when all this is waiting for you, when you know your ski days are numbered, when you know the frost won't be on the pumpkin much longer." He pulled the boot bindings tighter. "Call at night, in the middle of the night." He looked up at her and laughed. "You're on a vacation. Don't call at all. Pretend there are no phones."

She felt as though her heart was beating much too loudly and much too quickly. Sam was just saying innocent words and teasing her, but it was the way he said the words. What was happening to her? She never felt this way before. Maybe if Jason would tease her sometimes, maybe if he joked with her or laughed with her or made up funny stories. Katie shook her head. No, Jason wasn't the type.

"Hey, Miss Katie, how come you're shaking your head?"

She jerked her head slightly. She had been daydreaming again. Funny, that was happening a lot these past three days.

"Never mind, Sam. I was just thinking about something."

He put his hand on her arm. "Forget about it, whatever it is. Come on, the mountain's calling us."

It was! Magic Mountain! *Okay, here I come,* she said to herself as she moved forward slowly. There, Sam had already forgotten about yesterday. Now that it was bright sunshine, they were once again only two people on a late-winter vacation. Back to the fun!

On the snowy slopes she could be anyone she wanted to be — a jet-setter . . . an Olympic star . . . or an engaged schoolteacher from a small town in Maryland. On the slopes she was free to be herself. It was as though this was where she belonged forever. She had always felt this way, ever since she was a child and her father had put the small skis on her feet and helped guide her down a little hill near their home. "Look, Daddy," she had cried out as she moved the short distance. "I'm free." Those were the words she had used even then, and suddenly the grown-up Katie paused and looked down Magic Mountain. Funny that she should think of her father and of that almost-forgotten time. It was so long ago — long before he had started traveling, long before her parents' divorce. She shook her head. It was such a long time ago.

"You're doing it again, Katie-Katie." Sam was standing beside her. "Daydreaming again." He pushed off. "Come on, follow me!" he yelled, and she could hear his echo resounding through the pine trees flanking the runs.

He was right, her mind was a million miles away. She looked at him as he took off down the slopes. What was it about him that made her think of her parents and of the times the three of them had spent together? She started down the run, liking the feeling of the cold air stinging her cheeks, and the muffled sound of the skis racing through the packed snow. It was a comforting sound from her childhood, when she had been free.

"Good run, Katie." Sam was waiting for her at the bottom. "This is what everyone needs — a holiday." He flipped his sunglasses up and she could see his brown eyes gleam just before he turned and faced the sun and squinted. Even when he wrinkled his eyes like that, he looked like he was always going to have fun.

"Hey," he said, turning to watch her once more. "What say we do this again? And again?"

"And again?" she asked. "I already know you, Sam Hubbard. You're not going to stop even for lunch. Come on." She grinned and took hold of the bar. "Why waste the morning?"

"Oh, Katie," she heard him say from behind her, "I'm so glad I met you." She stared straight ahead, pretending that she hadn't heard him. She was glad that she was in front of him and he couldn't see the confused look on her face. He was doing it again, making her feel all sorts of emotions she had never felt before. She had to avoid that. She reached for the T-bar and held it tightly, as though by doing so she could squeeze away all the strange feelings that were stirring within her.

The sun was beginning to set behind the trees and the temperature was dropping rapidly. By the time they had been outside for six hours, Katie was exhausted and numb. They had had a quick bowl of soup as a lunch break and a chance to get warm, but aside from those thirty minutes they had spent the rest of the time on the slopes, enjoying the sport and each other.

"This has to be the very last one, Sam. I'm tired and I'm cold and —"

"And you're calling it a day. Okay, spoilsport, I'll give in too." He paused for a moment and looked at the few skiers left. "I like it when it gets like this. All the novices have given up. In fact, almost everyone has given it up. It's practically deserted."

She nodded. This was her time too, when she could call the mountain her own and could pretend she was the only one in the world. Only now there were two of them. Sam and Katie. Katie and Sam. Try as she might, she still couldn't put the memory of his kisses aside. Sam and Katie . . . Katie and Sam. Somehow it all seemed so natural.

The wind whipped around her, shaking her back to the present, interrupting her reverie and flinging snow against her face. She shivered from both the sudden wet cold on her face and her warm thoughts.

Sam saw her and understood only half the reason. "Hey, you really are cold, aren't you?" he said, and she didn't correct him. "Come on, this is the last one for us today." He picked up his poles. "What say we race to the lodge?"

"No way, Sam." She laughed. "You'd have the advantage. I'm so cold that my toes won't respond. Try me in the morning. That's when I'm at my best."

He looked at her and his eyes softened. "I haven't seen you at anything *but* your best these past couple of days."

She caught her breath. *Oh, Sam!* she thought.

What's happening to me? To us? She ducked her head once more and prepared to push off. She would call Jason as soon as she got to her room.

Chapter Five

The waiter put down their dinners in front of them and Katie watched as Sam began to unfoil the baked potato, again getting burned from the steam, exactly as had happened for the past three evenings. She watched him blow on his finger, and she smiled as she heard his "Darn it," remembering that he had done and said exactly the same thing every time he unwrapped his potato.

This was their third dinner together, and Katie realized that she was beginning to count the days left for them. Four more days, and then it was back to school and to Maryland and to Jason. Yes, she'd go back to Jason and — and that would be it. All this time with Sam would be a lovely memory — nothing but a lovely memory — and when she spoke the words in her mind, she felt her eyes mist slightly. She shut them, and when she opened them again, the haze was gone, but now she felt the small knot in the pit of her stomach as she repeated to herself that this would all be only a lovely memory.

She reached for the butter and started putting it on her potato. Looking at Sam, she wondered what he was thinking. Did he feel anything for her besides friendship? As he spooned globs of sour cream onto his potato, he saw her watching him and he smiled.

"Can't help it. I know all about cholesterol and all that stuff, but I love it. Anyhow, this is my vacation. I never eat like this on the road. I never have time. I'm too busy hopping on airplanes."

There, he had said it again — "on the road." There was something about those words that reminded her of all the times she had been alone and lonely while growing up. All those times her father had been away from home. She watched as Sam spread the sour cream across the top of the steaming potato, oblivious to her thoughts. Jason wouldn't travel much — schoolteachers were never shifted around that fast — and when he did go away, it would only be for a class trip or a vacation and she would probably be with him. She'd never be lonely with Jason.

She watched as the butter melted on her own potato and formed rivulets to the dish. No, Jason would always be around in case she needed him. She picked up her fork and held it, thinking that Sam had been quiet, too quiet. She glanced up for a second and saw him looking out the window at the mountain.

"You know what's happening to us, don't you Katie?"

Sam asked the question quietly, and for a moment she wasn't sure of his words, and when she realized what he had asked, she chose not to answer. She didn't want to answer. No, that wasn't correct. It was more than that — she didn't even want to think about what he was saying. It was too close to her own thoughts, and if she allowed herself to think about it, it would only present problems to her life. Problems that would hurt and confuse her.

"You know what's happening, Katie," he said again, and this time she knew that she had to answer him. But what could she say? She could deny what he was saying and what she had been thinking.

He said it a third time: "You know what I'm talking about, Katie, as sure as I do."

"Whatever it is, Sam, I don't want to talk about it." She put down her fork, afraid to eat, afraid that the food would stick in her throat like the words she really wanted to say.

He continued to look out the window. "We're falling in love, Katie. We *have* fallen in love," he corrected himself, acknowledging it as something that had already happened. He turned to look at her, and she saw his eyes, earnest and golden, questioning her,

59

searching her face for a confirmation of his words.

She shook her head. "We can't talk like this," she said, and added, "We mustn't."

"Why not?" He took her hand and held it. "Is it so wrong? Isn't that what happens when two normal, healthy adults meet, have fun, and then realize that there's something else about their relationship? An attraction, a very strong attraction to each other?" He pressed her hand. "You're feeling it too. I can tell." She tried to pull her hand away, but he held it. "You're attracted to me, Katie. I'm not alone in feeling it — you are too. Yesterday —"

"No . . . no, Sam. It's impossible."

"Why?" he asked, and then suddenly looked at her left hand. Are you married?" he asked hesitantly. "You never spoke about a husband." Carried away with the thought, he leaned against the back of his chair. "Hey, if I've overstepped, I'm sorry. I just thought that you were alone here and that there wasn't a Mr. Somebody in the picture."

Katie wanted to laugh and cry at the same time. She was touched by the way he had said it, the way he was worried that he had acted improperly. Another thing to like — love — about him in so short a time. She shook her head and said:

"No, there isn't a husband . . . not yet,

at least. But there's a man. Well, he's more than a man." She gulped and raced on: "I'm engaged, Sam. I'm going to be married." She didn't want to look at him anymore, and now it was her turn to stare through the window. "I didn't mention him before because I just didn't think anything would happen."

"You mean anything like falling in love with someone . . . with a stranger . . . with me?"

She nodded. "Yes. Oh, Sam! I've been here a dozen times, alone, and I've had a good time and — But I never met anyone who would. . . ." Her voice trailed off.

"Make you think twice about your fiancé?" He finished the sentence for her.

"Yes." She watched as a skier approached the window. "It just never happened before, that's all."

"And now that it has?"

Sam wasn't about to retreat, she realized, and she didn't quite know what to do or say. "I guess I don't know." She bit her lip. "This wasn't supposed to happen."

"Then you're saying that you feel it too?" He had a way of questioning and quickly getting at the answers, the truthful answers.

"Something like it." She wanted to tell him, *If feeling like you're happy and sad and confused and wanting to shout out to the world that you've got a sense of peace and amazement and how could anyone else ever have felt like this before is what you mean, then yes, yes, yes, I'm feeling it too. Whatever it is, it's affecting me too.*

"So what are we going to do about it, Katie?"

Again the direct question demanding an honest answer. Still staring at the window, she realized that she could see his reflection and his reaction to her words. He was sitting back in his chair — slumped against it, really — and she saw him tap the rim of his plate.

"I don't know," she said. "No, that's not true. Probably nothing. Probably I won't do anything about it."

"Nothing?" She saw his incredulous look. "You're just going to walk away from it? From us?" He shook his head. "I don't believe that, Katie. That's ridiculous — unbelievable. You just can't say that it's too bad it's happened." He picked up her hand again and gave it a little shake so that she turned toward him. "What kind of a woman are you, Katie, to want to put it all aside? To want to do nothing about it?" He scanned her face. "Don't you ever recognize your own feelings?"

She shivered. Sam had hit on a weakness she knew she had, her inability to act on her feelings. And he had discovered it in such a short time. It was true, she didn't want to recognize any strong feelings — love, hate, joy, sadness. Those were all perfectly good words to put in an English composition, but not to apply to life, at least not to her own life. She had had those feelings once upon a time, but the years she had spent with her parents — her mother, especially — and the times she had seen the look of unhappiness on her mother's face, made her resolve long ago not to give in to any feelings that she couldn't control. And this was one of those feelings.

"It's very mixed-up," she said, and she saw his eyes narrow as he drummed his fingers on the table. "Very mixed-up."

"Look at me, Katie," he said, so sharply that she blinked. "Do I look like some monster to you?" She shook her head. "Do I look like I want to hurt you?" She shook her head again. "Do I look like I want to take advantage of you?" For the first time in the conversation they both smiled. "No kidding," he said. "I'm really an honorable person. Okay, just tell me one thing. You do know that something happened out there yesterday, don't you? You do recognize something between us — some little spark?"

Yes, Sam, she wanted to say. *Yes, I know that there's something there. That's what the problem has been all day. That's why I tried to call Jason so many times. That's why I had to talk to him, wanted to hear his voice, to be reassured that he was my fiancé and that he was waiting for me, expecting me to return from just another winter vacation. Only, he wasn't there. Yes, Sam, I recognize that there's something there. But I don't want to. I really don't want to.*

He tried another tack: "Do you think it's just the fact that we're having a good time? Or that we met each other at some vulnerable moment for each of us? Or that we have so many things in common? Or" — he smiled — "all of the above?"

She tilted her head to one side and kept silent. *All of the above,* she wanted to shout. *All of the above and more.* But she didn't say anything, and they remained awkwardly quiet.

"Okay," Sam said, pushing his plate away. "We do have a problem, don't we?" His chest heaved. "So what do we do about it? What *can* we do about it?"

"Nothing. There's nothing we can do." Katie was miserable, and a tight band began to form around her head and compress it. This was something she hadn't bargained for, this was to have been just another vacation. It was supposed to be strictly skiing, strictly fun. Nothing was supposed to happen, and certainly nothing that would affect her life so permanently.

"Oh, Katie-Katie," he said, "we just can't turn our backs on this and pretend it never happened. It would be such a waste."

She had no answers. She rocked back and forth in her chair, her palm against her head, trying to push at the ache inside and outside her skull. She wanted the pounding to stop. Most of all she wanted to stand up and run from the room. But she couldn't, knowing in her heart that she really wanted to stay with Sam for as long as she had time left.

"Suppose you tell me about your fiancé," he said.

"What good would it do?"

"It would give me a fair chance."

She almost blurted out that it was she who needed the fair chance, that he had come along out of the blue and disturbed her very calm and orderly life just by smiling and talking with her.

"He's just someone I've known for a long time, a fellow teacher. I work with him at the same school. I've known him for years."

"Is he good to you?"

"Oh, yes, very good. He's a very nice person —very gentle, very orderly. Everyone likes him."

"Do you love him?"

She closed her eyes. He was asking the hard question now, and she didn't know how to answer him.

"Katie, do you love him? How come you can't answer that question? It's the one question you should be able to answer quickly and with feeling. It should be the easiest." He put his hand over hers. "You should be able to say, 'Yes, Sam, I love him very much.' But you don't. So I'll ask you again, Katie: Do you love him?"

"It's not like that, Sam. It's not like music and rainbows and balloons and craziness. Jason's not like that. He's stable and good, and he knows what he wants out of life. He does things in quiet ways and . . ."

"Katie, look at me." Sam's hand closed over hers, and she kept her eyes on his hand, watching as his fingers curled over hers. "Tell me that you love him, Katie-Katie, and I'll walk away now. Tell me that you want him, and I'll leave you alone. I'll leave Mountain Laurel this evening. Tell me that you don't love *me*." He waited, and when she didn't reply he ran his fingers lightly over hers, stroking them, smoothing them. "You can't, can you?"

She shook her head, knowing that she had to answer truthfully. "No." There — she had said it. It was there for both of them to know now.

"Okay, Katie," he said, tightening his grip on her and seeming to read her mind. "Tell me now that you love *me*."

"No!" Her voice was soft but clear. "I don't even know you. I can't say that. I won't say that."

"Then, Katie, in these next four days I'm going to make you know me and I'm going to get to know you. And then we'll see what you have to say." He squeezed her hand once more and then pointed it toward the mountain. "Come on, lady, it's still early and we've got a lot of skiing and . . . a lot of other things to do. Mind you, Katie, I'm a very good salesman and I mean to sell you on me."

As he pulled her from her chair, she glanced around to see if people were watching them. But no one was paying attention to them. They were just two guests at the lodge.

"Sam . . ." she began, but he held up his hands in front of him. "Don't say a word right now, Katie. We've got only four days. We'll talk later."

Chapter Six

When Jason finally answered the phone after ten rings, Katie was sure that he had been asleep, because it was almost one A.M. He liked getting a full eight hours of rest every night. It was something he was adamant about and something she used to tease him about, telling him that there were some people who needed only four hours' sleep and that they were perfectly capable of doing their jobs well. But Jason had only shaken his head, saying that he was always in bed before midnight and would always continue the practice except in an emergency. Well, maybe tonight could be considered an emergency, she thought. Tonight she had to talk to him and hear his voice. Surely he would understand.

"Hello, Jason." She tried to keep her voice light, not wanting to betray her real reason for calling, wanting to hear his familiar, low-pitched voice for an assurance that back in Maryland there was a reality transcending the ski slopes of Mountain Laurel, and that once this week was over, everything would return to normal at home.

"Hi, Katie," he said drowsily. "I didn't expect to hear from you this week. Is everything all right?"

"Sure. What could be wrong?" She creased her brow. If only she could tell him what the problem was — that another man had come into her life and was confusing her. "Jason, I —" she began, but he interrupted her before she could say another word:

"I wondered if you were having a good time, Katie. I figured it just might be too warm there for skiing. It's almost seventy degrees here."

"No, no," she assured him. "It's cold here and there's plenty of snow and skiing."

"That's good." Jason coughed. "I think the allergy season has started already. I even went to sleep early this evening."

"I'm sorry, I didn't mean to awaken you. I guess it is late, isn't it?"

"Are you just getting in, Katie?" He coughed again.

"No. I've been in awhile. I was just — just reading and I thought I would call you, just to see how you are." She paused, and when he made no response she continued: "I just wanted to. . . . What have you been doing, Jason?" If only he would say something romantic, tell her he missed her, say anything that would encourage her to think positive thoughts about them. *Oh, Jason!* she thought.

Tell me that you love me, really love me. Make me want to forget about Sam. Make me remember who you are — who we are — and what we'll be.

"It's been such great weather that I've gotten the team together for some early practice. Looks like we're going to have a great bench this year." Jason had never sounded more enthusiastic. "Wait till you see them."

"Yes." She paused, knowing that she should sound no less enthusiastic. It just wasn't Jason's style to say anything romantic. He let her know in practical ways that he cared for her. She sighed. What would happen if she just said something nice and simple like, "Jason, I've met a man . . ."? No, that wouldn't work. Why couldn't she just tell him that she was troubled, that Sam was intruding on her time, on their plans? No, better to tell him that in person, when she was able to think more lucidly. Then, maybe, she wouldn't have to tell him about Sam. Maybe being away from Sam would make her realize that she really loved Jason. She cleared her throat. "Well," she said, "I just wanted to see how you were doing. Take care of yourself, Jason. I'll be home in three days."

"Yep. I'll pick you up at the airport. Happy skiing, Katie."

She heard him hang up, and she stood there

holding the telephone, annoyed that she had accomplished nothing except awakening Jason. She knew that he would go back to sleep and not think about the telephone call anymore. He was like that. He would just think that she was lonely and needed some reassurance from him. No, Jason would have no misgivings about her calling him, because, as far as he was concerned, everything was always on course. Nothing could or would interfere with their lives.

She slowly shook her head. Jason would never understand her confusion at this point, at this early stage of a — what could she call it? — a flirtation? A fascination? A romance? What could she call what was happening between her and Sam?

She continued to hold the receiver in her hand, oblivious of it, and she was startled when the operator asked her if she wanted to place another call. "No . . . no," she said, and hung up the phone and stood looking at it, wishing that Jason could have read her mind, and wishing that he would call her back and ask her if anything was really wrong. But she knew Jason wasn't like that. He was probably sound asleep again.

She sat in the chair next to her bed and thought about the evening . . . about how Sam hadn't said another word to her about

71

the two of them, and how she was able to forget that she was becoming more trapped in a triangle. Sam had told her about his family — his sister and parents — and how both children were taught to ski at an early age because his parents believed in fresh air and cold air naturally meant fresh air. He had said, making her laugh, "You should have seen us, Katie. There we were, shivering, and my mother kept saying, 'It's good for you, it's good for you.' And all my sister and I wanted to do was go inside and drink hot chocolate."

And afterward, Sam had taken her arm when they had tired of the slopes, and he guided her into the coffee shop and ordered hot chocolate for them. "To this day, Katie, every time I think of a mug of this, I automatically look around for my skis and poles, and I honest to goodness can smell wet woolen mittens and almost hear my mother encouraging us, and I remember how cold my nose was all the time and all those other little crazy things you keep stored in your mind because they were so much fun once upon a time."

Katie had sat there, warmed by the fire in the stone fireplace, watching him as he drank from the mug, and she could almost see him as he was twenty-five or so years ago, shivering and then blowing on the hot steam. Much like he did with the baked potato, she thought, and then she remembered the scene in the restaurant when he had told her that he thought they were falling in love.

She had to talk about something else then, so that the memory of the simple but powerful statement could be erased, and she spoke about the other guests and how she had recognized some of them from past vacations. "That's the fun of coming to the same place year after year," she had said. "You get to feel like it's old home week." And then she put her head down and bit her lip because she knew that he would never be able to call Mountain Laurel a regular place, a regular ski resort of his. His traveling would make that impossible.

His traveling — that was one of the big stumbling blocks in the whole relationship. They were two different types, and he had even said it. He was the wanderer and she had called herself a homebody, a person who found her peace and contentment at a home base. That was her life, that was what she had always wanted.

She shook her head once more and then glanced at the clock. It was late and she wanted to be up early tomorrow. Magic Mountain was constantly beckoning her now, reminding and warning her that only a few more days were left. It was as if the mountain radiated a magic

73

of both joy and sadness, and after she and Sam left, the spell would be broken forever. As she switched off the light, she remembered what Sam had said about memories, and she wondered if, years from now, she would be just another person and this just another pleasant week stored in his mind.

Chapter Seven

Katie couldn't remember when she'd been so happy or so sad. The days and evenings with Sam were exciting and joyous, and constantly filled with new and bright conversation. By day they skied the mountain and trails, and in the evening, after dinner, they would linger at the table and talk about their lives.

"Tell me about your family," Sam said when they first sat down at the table. "I don't know a thing about you." He reached for her hand and caressed it. "And I want to know all about you." She let her hand remain in his, liking the way it fitted within his fingers and palm. It was a large hand, almost as though it belonged to a pianist. The fingers were long and slender, and she wondered if he preferred Beethoven or the Beatles. It was something to ask him later.

"Well," she began, in answer to his question, "there's just my mother and me," and she was grateful that he accepted the statement and didn't ask about her father. "She lives in Alabama near a lot of aunts and cousins, and she's having a wonderful time. She's one of those very active social women, the kind who like getting involved with gardening, clubs, social activities, and all that. She always did. People would always say that she had class and style, if you know what I mean." She looked at her own jeans and heavy sweater. "She wouldn't approve of this outfit, for instance. It's not quite feminine enough for her," she said, laughing. "I get to see her a few times a year, and we always have a good time. Only. . . ." She looked up at Sam and laughed again. "We both like to get our own way, and so we're both stubborn. But aside from that — her trying to influence me and my trying to not let her — we get along really well." She looked outside at the softly falling snow. "She loves warm weather, I like cold, and never the twain shall meet."

"Just as long as you both have your own lives." Sam put down his fork. "It's a live-and-let-live world, Katie."

She nodded. "Yes, I know, but try telling her that sometimes. So that's why I live alone. I'm happier this way and so is she. Not that I don't love her — don't get me wrong — but sometimes it's very difficult." She shook her head. "We really are very different except for one thing." She put her hands close to her lashes. "Everyone knows we're mother and daughter when they see our eyes. The same color, the same deep brown. But I also

76

look a lot like my dad."

"Tell me about him."

Should she tell him about her father? About how she had really loved him, although she hadn't gotten to see him too often? She heard Sam drumming his fingers against the table — one of his habits when he was thinking about something. It was funny how much Sam reminded her of her father. Maybe that was why she was attracted to him. And maybe that was why, also, she was attracted to Jason. He and her father had nothing — no, absolutely nothing — in common. Her father was spur-of the-moment; Jason was methodical. And sometimes that was good — he planned for everything and anything. There would never be worries about anything practical when they married.

She took a deep breath. *When she and Jason were married.* Funny, but that idea seemed so remote today. She could see Sam's fingers drumming on the table now. The fingers beat a cadence that seemed to say, *Sam is here, Sam is here. Jason isn't, Jason isn't. What to do? What to do?*

"Katie-Katie, come back to Mountain Laurel," Sam said softly, and she smiled at him. "I was asking you about your dad."

"Ah, my dad." Katie put her elbows on the table and her head on her hands. "It's very difficult for me to talk about him."

"Look, if I've upset you — hey, don't answer it. It's just something I wanted to know about you, to try to fit all the pieces of the Katie Jarvis puzzle together. So that I can know you better." He leaned back against the slats of his chair. "Oh, Katie love, we have so much to discover about each other."

"And so little time," she murmured.

"Don't say that, Katie. We still have three days. I told you I'm a convincing salesman. That's my job, to sell ideas and plans, and now you're my biggest client and I'm my biggest plan. If you say yes, then I take over the company."

Katie shifted in her seat and smiled. "You would have liked my father. He was a lot like you. A lot like you," she repeated, and let her voice drop: "He was even a salesman. And he could sell anything."

"What happened to him?"

"He died a few years ago. It was very complicated, Sam. You see, he and my mother divorced when I was twelve and it crushed me. He was a shining beacon to me, someone I could focus on when I was supposed to be studying in class and I got bored. I could always think that today was Wednesday or Thursday and I would see him soon. Fridays were pure magic for me."

She smiled as she remembered herself as a young girl. "And every time he came home on the weekend — that's the only time I saw him even when we were all living together, because he was away traveling the territory during the week — well, anyway, I would wait for him because he would bring me back things. Not necessarily material things — it was more than that. He would bring me back stories about the people he met and the cities and towns he visited, and he would tell me about them and, oh, Sam, there were some nights I would go to bed thinking that his had to be the best life in the world. He surely had to be the luckiest person in the world to have such a great job. That was when I thought traveling was the best thing you could do, the only thing. That's because my dad made it appear that way."

She looked away toward the window and saw that it was snowing harder now, and she remembered that the lodge's weather forecaster had predicted a brief storm that evening.

"Well, anyway," she went on, "the strain and stress of not having a husband around all the time got to my mother, and she finally told me one day — I'll never forget, it was a Friday and I was looking forward to seeing him — that she and Dad had decided to live apart from then on." She touched the rim of her cup and moved her finger around it. "It hurt her, Sam. She isn't a callous person even though I accused her of sending him away, and it hurt her to say that to me. She made the decision for both of them — I know she did — but she had her reasons and I really do understand them now. But try telling a twelve-year-old girl that her father isn't coming home anymore. It was terrible."

He nodded. "It must have been," he said quietly, and she could tell that he meant the words, felt compassion.

"I could see her point, Sam. She wanted a husband and a home and family, and she wanted them all together, under the same roof, every night, every day. It wasn't the same, seeing him only on weekends. At least not for her. As for me, I had my friends, but Mother wanted more than friends. She needed a husband's companionship, and she wasn't able to get it from my father. It was just the circumstances, the way it was. She figured that she was married and entitled to have someone to rely on, for whatever reasons. She wanted her husband home with her." She looked up at Sam. "We're a lot alike on that score."

He signaled the waiter for more coffee, and they were silent while the cups were refilled. He took a sip of the coffee and closed his eyes slightly. His mouth worked for a few seconds before he said, "So that's why you said we could never. . . ." He shook his head.

She nodded. "You're so much like my father. He would have loved you."

"I wish that *you* would." He said it simply and directly, and she felt a shiver run through her body. How could she say she didn't love him? She was telling him things she had never told anyone, not even Jason. It was just so easy to talk to Sam, to tell him about her life and her hurts. No, she could never deny to herself that she loved him — she did very much — although she had known him less than a week. Only this was a no-win situation. Hadn't she seen her mother hurt? Surely she had learned something from her mother's experience.

"Did you get to see your father often?" He was probing now, seeking information that might reconcile their situations.

"Yes, on weekends. Our time together was limited. He still told me stories and sent me postcards, but I gradually saw the change in him. It was like the spark had gone out of him. And I began to hate the traveling he did and the cards he sent me." She stared at the near-empty dining room. "It was terrible, Sam. I started to realize that if he had a job like the other fathers in my neighborhood — well, then I would have had a father too. But

I also knew that to force him to take a job nearer home would only cage him, and I didn't want that, either. I loved him too much to ask him to do that." She touched his hand. "I don't want that to happen to me again, Sam. I don't want to be lonely in my adult life too. Can you understand?"

He slumped in his chair for a few moments, and then sat up again. "What makes you think we'd have the same kind of marriage? It doesn't have to be that way, you know."

"Are you asking me to give up my career?"

"No, but with your job and mine, the weekends that we spend together, and the vacations, too, will only be better for us. We'll appreciate each other more. Your mother didn't have a job — that's why she was so lonely. We'd handle our lives differently."

"Uh-uh." She shook her head and folded her hands in front of her. "That would last for only a few years — two or three at the most — and then what? No, Sam, I meant it. It just wouldn't work with us."

"Would it work with your . . . ?"

She knew he meant Jason, and she replied quietly, "Yes."

"He's steady."

"Very."

"And he's always there?"

"Always."

As he wrinkled his brow, it seemed to her that he was trying to fit into place all the pieces of a difficult puzzle. "But, Katie, the most important ingredient in any relationship is love."

"There are all kinds of love, and sometimes even more is needed in a marriage." She was on the defensive. His questions were ones she had asked herself these past nights, and she had no answers yet. She had to prove to Sam, and to herself, that Jason was the man she should marry.

"Name some other things. What else is important?"

"Mutual respect, for one." Suddenly her voice was louder.

"I certainly respect you! And I assume the feeling is mutual."

How she wished he would laugh or smile. But he was so serious — so very serious. She said, "Jason and I are good friends."

"I'm your friend too, Katie."

She closed her eyes, wishing that she didn't have to continue, wishing that it was a year from now and that this episode was in the past. But when she opened them, she saw Sam staring at her, waiting for her to speak. "I know you are, Sam, but Jason and I go back a long way. We have the same ideals and values."

"Don't I have the same values too? Don't I want the same things as you? Don't I want to love you for the rest of your life, Katie-Katie? And to make you happy, to make us both happy?"

She took a deep breath, hoping to still the panic rising within her. *This isn't fair!* she wanted to cry out. *A woman shouldn't have to choose between two good men. It should all be clear-cut. There shouldn't be these problems, these trials.*

"Come away with me," Sam said.

"Just like that, Sam?" The absurdity of the suggestion made her laugh. "I have so much to clear up. I could never walk away from my life."

"Clear it up and *then* come away with me."

She shook her head. Her heart seemed to break when she saw his dark eyes focus on her, taking in everything she said and did so that he seemed to consume her mind and thoughts.

"I can't. That's what's different about us, Sam. I'm practical. Very practical."

"And I'm . . .?" From the way he said it, she knew he saw himself as someone who was spontaneous, someone who would try all possible ways to succeed in love, life, and his profession. "And I'm . . .?" he asked again, so that she wanted to answer him that she had never met anyone quite like him before. He was someone who would never give up fighting for what he wanted.

She opened her mouth to speak, and tried to form words so that she could put her thoughts in order. But her emotions overcame her practicality, and she was finally content to think the words that assembled much too quickly in her consciousness. *You're wonderful*, she wanted to cry out. *You're what I always wanted. You're the person I have dreamed about all my life, the Prince Charming in all the fairy tales I ever read. The hero who comes riding on a horse to rescue me. You're all those things I've dreamed about, and you're all those things that I want and all those things I don't want. Oh, Sam! If I could, I would tell you that I love you, with all my heart. And that I want to run away with you and live any kind of existence with you. But I can't. I can't afford to get hurt. I have to be practical. I think of all those things we could do, but all the things we couldn't do outweigh them.*

These were the things she wanted to say but was unable to. Instead, she shook her head. "You're different from me, Sam. Let's leave it at that," she said, and then felt another wave of indecision, so that her hands began to tremble and a violent shudder hit the pit of her stomach.

She took a deep breath to calm herself and waited until the shaking had passed through her body. "Sam, please . . ." she said quietly, almost pleadingly. "Let's not do this to each other. Let's talk about it some other time, when we've thought about it some more."

He picked up her hand once again and caressed it. "We don't have that much time, Katie. We just don't have that much time. And I'm afraid I'm going to lose you if we don't talk."

She looked outside at the snowflakes swirling near the windows. "Please, Sam," she said, "please . . . let's talk tomorrow." She stood up and glanced at her watch and then at the deserted room. "The waiters . . ." she said, indicating two men in the doorway. "They want to close."

He stood up, too, and took her arm. "I didn't mean to press you so hard, Katie." His arm surrounded her waist, and he drew her close to him as they walked slowly toward the steps to the rooms on the upper floor. "You're exhausted and so am I. Maybe tomorrow will bring us some answers."

"Yes." He was right; already he could read her mind. She was very tired and wanted to sleep, to close her eyes and force unwelcome thoughts away from her.

He stopped on the landing of the second

floor and put his hands on the sides of her face so that their eyes were locked. She wanted to turn away, because to look at him would confuse her even more. She wasn't falling in love with Sam. She already *had* fallen in love with him. And the more she was with him, the more she wanted to stay near him.

"Promise me, Katie, that you'll think about everything — us . . . you . . . Jason. And that you'll have an open mind about everything." He kissed her lightly on the forehead, and when she didn't respond, he moved his head nearer and kissed her lips lovingly. "Promise," he said, and kissed her again.

She put her arms around him and held him tight, wanting to hold him forever. "I promise, Sam."

"That's all that I ask."

Inside her room, she stood for a few minutes at the door, leaning against it for support, and then, tired, she sat down on the edge of the bed and rocked slowly back and forth, thinking that life had seemed so simple only last week. And now. . . .

Later, after a distant clock tolled three times, she managed to fall asleep. All night, Sam and his words and his questions kept drifting in and out of her dreams.

Chapter Eight

When they met for breakfast, she could tell that he had slept as fitfully as she. His eyes were ringed with dark circles and some of their gleam was missing. She turned away, not wanting to see the hurt she was causing him, and she looked at the other people in the room, hoping to find a way to avoid talking about themselves.

"There are a lot of new skiers," she said, motioning toward the line waiting to be seated for breakfast. "I guess they heard about the snowfall last night."

"Which means that the slopes are going to be crowded." He buttered a piece of toast "Why don't we go over to Devil's Mist? Not too many beginners on that one." He took a sip of coffee.

"No, it's not for me." Katie's throat tightened. She had successfully avoided that ski trail before, and no one — not even Sam — would make her change her mind.

"You're afraid of it, aren't you, Katie?" It was one of his direct-on-target statements, and she said nothing. He buttered another piece of toast while she tried to decide whether to admit the truth. "You keep avoiding it. That's not the way to conquer it." He smiled, and she had the feeling that he was talking about their relationship. "You have to just get up there, go straight to the top, and then come on down the best way you know how, one ski at a time." He ate the toast. "You're a good skier, so what's the problem?"

"I don't like Devil's Mist," she said finally. "I never have."

"Why?" Sam cocked his head.

"It's just that it's difficult, more difficult than Magic Mountain."

"It's not for beginners. That's what's so good about it. It takes more skill and more daring. Some things you have to work for, Katie. Some things aren't easy."

She wiped her lips with her napkin. Was he purposely saying things that could be taken two ways? "I just don't like that run," she said.

"You're avoiding it, Katie. Just like. . . ." He stopped in midsentence, yet she knew what he was going to say. He was going to talk about her avoiding the ski run just as she was avoiding their love. She took a sip of coffee. Well, why not? Why not try to ski the mountain again? Maybe it wasn't so frightening anymore. Maybe it was all in her mind. She'd try it one more time, and if she still felt uncomfortable when she got to the top, then she'd come down any way she wanted to, no matter what anyone said.

She tapped her spoon against her coffee cup, oblivious to the ringing sound of the pottery. She'd conquer one thing at a time, and maybe if this battle was won, she could think about the other, more personal one, and come to some conclusions. Maybe she'd get back some of her confidence and be able to make some new choices.

She looked at Sam and tried to laugh. "Okay," she said, "I'll try it." His eyes flashed briefly, the way they did when they first met. "We'll go there after breakfast, before I lose my nerve. After all, it's only my life."

Sam stared at her. "Sounds like foreshadowing," he said.

She turned her head so that he couldn't see the confirmation in her eyes. It was the second time that he had linked the mastery of the mountain to the events of the week. But then again, maybe he was right, maybe Devil's Mist had something to do with her life and the way she handled it.

She stood up. "I'll get my skis."

Sam had called it perfectly. Magic Mountain was crowded with novices who had heard last night's weather forecast. It was natural, then, for the accomplished skiers to seek out other runs, and Devil's Mist was the only really good one in the immediate area.

It seemed much higher and larger than she remembered it from two seasons ago, and she could see why so many people wanted to ski it. It was the challenge of it, the thrill of it. Devil's Mist was tricky and fast, and it was a way of extending the excitement of the sport. Well, perhaps today she would conquer her old nemesis. She tightened her boots and positioned the poles on her arm. *Okay,* she thought. *Possibly today I'll do it. Maybe Sam will be my inspiration.*

He was waiting for her to join him, and she saw that there were only three or four other people on the lifts. "Okay, Katie," he said, adjusting his goggles. "Let's get on with it. It's a perfect day for it." He looked around. "Not even a line." He took her arm and propelled her into a chair so that her feet and poles dangled high over the ground and she could get an overview of the vista below her.

"Wait until you get up there." He climbed onto the adjoining seat as he pointed up to the top. "I guarantee you the best run of the week. Be warned, Katie — you're in for the ride of your life."

Katie looked down at the countryside as the lift moved slowly up the mountain. Sam was right — again. After her initial panic, which had blotted out all other thoughts from her mind, she was now able to see the breathtaking beauty of the setting as the lift skimmed the tops of the tall evergreens below. The panorama suddenly seemed extraordinarily serene and quiet, and as she approached the top of the mountain, all manner of sounds — shouts, laughter, voices — were first hushed and then completely stilled. Her eyes and ears captured the scene and framed it much like a still life painted by a folk artist. Off in the distance the main lodge now seemed frozen in time, its only sign of life the curls of black smoke streaming from its chimneys. In front of the stone-and-wood inn and on either side of it, bright splotches of color punctuated the white and gray landscape as vacationers in vivid ski-wear loitered and walked in the snow.

Katie marveled at the sight. Why hadn't she ever looked at the valley like this before? Was it because Sam was here beside her, because he was her guide and was now making her see commonplace things in a different light? Maybe that was the reason, she thought as her fear of the mountain vanished and she concentrated on the landscape beneath her.

"Was I right? Didn't I tell you it was magnificent?" Sam shouted so that she could hear him above the wind. "Who would believe that the calendar says it's spring?"

Spring? Katie's stomach clenched. Jason had said that it was really spring in Maryland, that it was warm and that the forsythia bushes and crocuses had already begun to blossom. She looked below her at the snow-capped shrubs and trees, and tried to imagine what it was like back home in Maryland. Warm already, spring weather, and soon it would be April and June and then August, the month when she and Jason would marry. August! They had tentatively set the date for that month because then they would have time for a two-week honeymoon before classes began again in mid-September. She wrinkled her brow as she thought of summer and what it held for her.

"Hey, Katie-Katie!"

Hearing Sam's voice, she turned and saw him laughing and motioning off to the distance. "Katie, my love," he shouted, "you've been away again." He spread his arms to encompass the entire view. "Look at it. Remember it. We should have taken a camera with us."

How could she ever forget this moment? It would be impossible. She would always treasure it. No matter what happened throughout her life, it was something she couldn't and wouldn't ever forget. She would always remember this place and time . . . and especially

Sam. If only she had met him earlier. She swallowed hard, hoping to rid herself of the pain that seemed to be crushing her heart.

"New tracks to be made, Katie!" Sam yelled as the lift came to a lurching halt. "Come on."

He guided her to the back of the mountain, where he said, "This is the best run. It's the one that takes your breath away — literally." He laughed. "This is the one you have to try. It's exciting, and dangerous, and conquerable." She shivered as he described it. "And how you can stay at Mountain Laurel and never attempt this run, I can't imagine."

As he grinned at her, she forced herself to smile. One more thing to like about him — his enthusiasm, his zest for life even when he was troubled.

She stood poised at the top of the peak, looking down at the scene he indicated, and she caught her breath at its magnificence. She had never been on this far side of Devil's Mist, and she pushed her poles into the snow in order to stay absolutely still and look at it in its entire splendor. From where she stood, it was a long, steep run to the base of the mountain, and it was punctuated by large stands of firs and cedars. The trees stood tall and formidable in their places, giving shelter and protection in snowstorms, but warned bewitched skiers to stay clear of their domain.

The terrain was tricky and deceptive, and to a novice it would look like a fairly straight run. But the experienced skier would recognize that scattered over the mountainside, in addition to the trees, were large formations of rock. Half hidden by the deep snow, they jutted up from the earth and shimmered and glinted in the cold sunlight. She blinked her eyes and adjusted her sunglasses to compensate for the extraordinary brightness. The absolute whiteness of the snow and the gleaming, brilliant crystals over all the mountain had become yet another photograph in her mind. There were so many memories to take back with her, so many bittersweet memories to recall through the years.

"Well, what do you think?" Sam touched her elbow. "Ready to try it?"

She shook her head. "Not yet, Sam. I'm just looking at it . . . wondering." She blew into the frigid air and saw puffs of vapor in front of her face.

"Don't wonder, Katie. Do it. I'll go down first if you want me to, and I'll stop halfway and wait for you."

She shook her head again. "I need a few more minutes."

"Katie, some days you just have to go ahead and do it!" Sam's voice was gentle yet urgent. "Sometimes, you just have to go ahead and do something without thinking of all the consequences. You have to jump in and participate. You can't stand back and wait, Katie, because sometimes. . . ." His voice grew fainter so that she had to strain to hear him: "Because sometimes you lose everything if you hesitate too long."

She knew that he was angry and impatient and hurt by her reluctance. She moved closer to the edge of the run and took another deep breath, planning how she would take the trail. If she traversed the slope and angled all the way to the base of the mountain, then she shouldn't encounter any difficulty. She would have to watch out for the trees, though. She looked at the cedars and tried to gauge the distance of the branches that overhung the trail. Though tricky, it really shouldn't be that difficult. She had the competence that came of having been on skis for almost all her life.

She took another deep breath as a gust of wind blew frozen flakes across her goggles, and she waited while the air calmed. She knew that Sam was watching her, waiting for her to make her move, and she inched a step closer to the edge so that she was now in position. She looked down the slope — no one was in sight — and suddenly another blast of wind swept first through the cedars and then up the incline.

Just go down it, Katie, she told herself. *Just pretend it's Magic Mountain.* She paused to brush away the snow from her face, and then slowly shook her head. It was no use. She couldn't do it. Her body was rigid and her feet suddenly felt leaden, rooted to the earth as though they were foreign objects that refused to obey her orders. She tried to flex her arms, but again her extremities wouldn't comply. Her hands were clenched tightly around the ski poles and she could feel the moisture trapped on her palms by her nylon mitts. No, today wasn't the day she would conquer Devil's Mist. It had won again!

"I'm sorry, Sam," she said simply. "I just can't do it. I don't know why." She waved her hands helplessly. "It just seems so . . . so. . . ."

"Fearful, Katie . . . fearful." He reached out to her and held her so that she felt comforted by both his warmth and his tenderness. "It's okay. Sometimes there are things we just can't do yet . . . no matter what." He put his arm around her shoulders and gave her scarf a gentle twist. "We still have a couple of days. We'll try again some other time."

She shook her head, angry at herself. Some things, whether mastering Devil's Mist or telling Sam she loved him, were just too difficult. Maybe some things weren't meant to be!

Chapter Nine

"Today, Katie," Sam said after breakfast, "I'm going to give you what I call breathing room. I told you I was going to treat you like a priority client, and I am, and this is what I do after I make my presentation. I give the client time to think, to weigh all the options, to get all the questions ready. And it gives me time to gather more ammunition to counter the questions and the doubts." He grinned at her, and she caught her breath at the simple gesture. "Yes, ma'am, you're my number-one client — and my only one — this week." He took her hand. "I've given you all the reasons for us to be together and to spend the rest of our lives with each other, and I really don't have anything else to offer." He spread his hands wide and stepped back so that she could see him in full view. "Look at me, Katie-Katie. What you see is what you get."

She wanted to tell him that she liked — loved — what she saw, and that if their timing had been right, she wouldn't hesitate. But Jason had been there first and Jason was steady and would always be home. And it wasn't as though she didn't like Jason. How could she be sure that this wasn't just a fleeting romance? She recounted to herself all the reasons for her decision to stay with Jason. But she had to admit, looking at Sam's impish smile, that there was a time bomb in her head, and it kept reminding her that perhaps she was making a mistake, was just settling for something safe and secure. She remembered a story she had once read about a person who had to detonate an explosive. One false move and the whole cruise ship would blow up. That's how she felt about Sam and Jason. One false move on her part and she would give in to her emotions and tell Sam that she wanted and needed him. But as long as she took things slowly, like an expert defusing a bomb, then nothing would go wrong . . . could go wrong.

"You're away again, Katie," she heard him say through her thoughts.

She blinked. "Sorry. I told you it was a habit."

"That's your one permitted escape, isn't it?" he said. "No, don't answer that — erase it. I promised nothing heavy today, and I meant it. Let's go to the souvenir shop again. I've got to get something." He looked out the window at the lines already formed for Magic Mountain. "There are too many people there already. We'll hit it when they slack off for lunch."

It was almost deserted in the shop, and they browsed at the counters, picking up the little ornaments, playing with the windup toys, squeezing the plush animals with whistles in their stomachs, and reading the children's books. They were being silly, she knew, but it was the fun of it that she enjoyed. It was as if she had been set free; she could say or do anything and Sam would understand. She was beginning to learn that it was part of his nature to want to have fun, to want to do things spontaneously, and to want to include other people in his circle of joy.

"Look at this, Katie," he said, dangling a pull-toy train. "Did you ever have a set of trains?" When she shook her head, he continued, "No, that's what I thought. You were a traditional girl, with dolls and —"

"— cutouts and skates," she cut him off, finishing for him. She laughed. "I had only what you would call 'all-girl stuff.' "

"Uh-uh, Katie. No way. Every kid had skates." He put the toy back on the counter. "Unisex things don't count — bubble pipes, board games, jigsaw puzzles."

"I still do puzzles. I have one on my dining-room table right now. I go back to it every once in a while." She put her hand to her mouth and sighed. It was another reminder — Sam wouldn't have jigsaw puzzles on his dining room table. He was too busy traveling and didn't really have a home base to return to every day. He'd never get back to them except on weekends, if he were lucky. It was another indication that he wasn't for her. So many signs told her that he wasn't for her, that Jason was much more like her. They kept cropping up at the wrong times and places.

Sam didn't notice the change in her mood, and he walked around the store, picking up toys and scented soaps and games. She watched him as sunlight, streaming through the window, gilded his hair and parka as he bent forward to inspect a glass figurine. He grinned as he looked at the base and said:

"I saw the same thing in Italy. That's where this was made. You get to see the same things in all the countries, Katie. Makes you realize how small the world really is."

But the world really isn't that small, Sam, she wanted to say. *Certainly it's not small enough to accommodate both our plans.*

She trailed her hands over several wooden carvings, and suddenly realized that she was at the counter where she had met him just a few days ago, and that the tinkling sounds that filled the area were coming from several music boxes. Unable to resist them, she turned their keys so that the music coming from all the boxes at once mingled in a cacophony of different tempos and melodies. She stood there enchanted until they finally ran down.

She picked up a miniature musical china clock and marveled at the intricate, delicate cream-and-pink roses. She fingered the raised petals and closed her eyes as she tried to recall an image from another time. The pattern of the flowers and the pastel colors were reminiscent of something, a picture frame or a piece of ribbon she had once owned. But she shook her head and gave up; it was too long ago to remember, and she let the memory slip from her mind. Another reminder, maybe, of her and Sam. Perhaps, one day, he would slip from her mind too.

She held the clock in her hand, wondering about its melody, and, unable to resist, wound it up and waited for its tune. She recognized it instantly — *"Un Bel Dì, Vedremo"* from *Madame Butterfly* — and she recalled that the senior music class had performed it at an evening assembly at the end of last year. She hummed the familiar aria as she replaced the clock on the counter, thinking that Jason had been sitting next to her at that assembly, and that it was about then that they began to talk about getting married. After the program, she recalled, while walking to his car, they had spoken to some of the students. The kids had stared at them, and she could tell that they were wondering if Mr. King and Ms. Jarvis were going together. They had both laughed at the students' whispering.

"Might as well do it, Katie," Jason had said in the car. "The kids think we're an item, so I guess we are." He had held her hand. "How does that suit you, Katie?" he asked, and she said that it was fine with her. And that's how it was and how it progressed until they came up with August as a month. It wasn't really any big deal . . . nothing to really get excited about, although her mother had said, "Why wait?" Now she wondered, *Why did I wait?* If she had gotten married sooner, there would have been no vacation in March . . . no Sam . . . and no confusion.

She looked at the clock and was surprised to see that while the notes played the tiny gilt-edged minute hand swept the face of the clock quickly, so that it appeared to be counting down the hours. For a moment she was spellbound by the idea — until she realized that the miniature hand was also counting down her time with Sam.

She stared at the spinning dial. The combination of the poignant music and the reminder of the rapid passage of time was much too overwhelming for her, and she again felt the bitter lump form in her throat. She swallowed back a sob and looked up at the ceiling of the store, at its old-fashioned light fixture and fan, trying hard to concentrate on them, hoping that by doing so her tears would be absorbed back into her eyes and not betray her emotions. But it wasn't to be, and she wiped her face with her hand. As the clock wound down, she felt that with every prolonged note, the aria was reminding her of her choices.

Sam came over to her and wordlessly handed her a handkerchief.

"Oh, Sam," she said, "I have to go back, I can't stay here." She ran to the door of the shop. "Please don't follow me. Please let me be alone for now," she pleaded. She looked at the handkerchief and saw her pink lipstick on it, and she crumpled it into a ball and shoved it into her pocket. "This isn't fair!" she cried. "This isn't fair to either of us."

She ran out of the shop, not looking back, but knowing that Sam was respecting her wishes. She had to be alone now. There were too many things she had to think about, too many things that had to be sorted out before tomorrow.

Chapter Ten

Sam stuck to his pact that evening. "I promised you, Katie, and I meant it — no hard sell today." He put his finger under her chin and tilted it so that her face was close to his, too close for her comfort. "Are you okay?" he asked, and when she nodded her head he smiled. He looked closer at her swollen eyes, and she knew he was just being gallant. No, she wasn't okay and he knew it. They both knew it.

He touched her arm. "Of course, what you're thinking I don't know, and what I'm thinking you won't know, but we'll keep it light." He squeezed her hand. "This evening it's your choice. Whatever you want to do — dance, ski, talk, or walk — it's your choice. And," he said, grinning, "if you want to ski Devil's Mist even though I don't, then, of course, I'll do it. Anything for you."

She managed to smile when he mentioned Devil's Mist. That was another thing about him — he had a charm that could make her laugh even though her heart was breaking . . . like now.

"Come on," he said, drawing her away from

the dinner table. "Take your choice. What's it to be?"

"Ski, and not Devil's Mist," she said with a laugh. "Oh, Sam, sometimes you're completely — completely. . . ." She bit her lip, trying to find the right word to describe him. How could she ever describe him?

"Completely what?" He saw her confusion and stepped toward her. "Still your choice, Katie," he said.

She took it for a double statement. "The mountain," she said.

He bent his head in agreement. "Okay. Wherever . . . whatever you want."

She knew that he was making an avowal that went way beyond this moment. This evening was just what she wanted and needed. Sam, in his gentle and brash wisdom, was making no demands on her, never once mentioning their future. It was a strain for both of them, but Sam would always keep his promises, no matter what.

Jason was like that too, she had to admit. Once his word was given, then nothing could deter him. Maybe that was why she was attracted to both Sam and Jason — they did have some similar qualities. They were both kind and gentle human beings, and both were successful and happy in what they wanted to do in life. But, unfortunately, they both expected her to love them. And that was the problem. In her heart she knew that she loved them, but not in the same committed and romantic way. Right now it was too difficult to admit. Suppose that she chose for the wrong reasons?

This was one of the few times in her life that she had ever had to make a hard choice. Usually, she was able to decide within minutes, which was sometimes her trouble, she had been told. She sometimes made decisions too quickly. But this time — dealing with both her heart and mind — this was too complex . . . too painful. There was no logical right or wrong. Jason had always said to use your mind when you had to decide something. But this wasn't strictly a mental problem. Oh, no! This was a matter of her heart too. Why did she have to meet up with two really wonderful men? Why did she have to choose between them?

She had a jumble of disconcerting thoughts while waiting for Sam to finish his run and watching for his red cap and ski jacket to appear on the horizon. She had gone down first, in incredibly short time, and when she pushed off, he was still adjusting his boots. No matter. Waiting for him in the cold air would give her a chance to think.

Not that she hadn't already done a lot of

thinking this afternoon. She had skipped lunch and stayed in her room, not wanting to see Sam. She had even tried to call Jason again. Actually, she had played that children's game of thinking that if he answered, then it would be right to continue with their plans, and if he didn't answer, then she would break their engagement.

She let the phone ring twice before hanging up, not really wanting to take a chance on the result of the game. She would never know whether he was there or not. But it wasn't the way to decide the rest of your life! Definitely not! She smiled wryly. How would she ever tell anyone — Jason, Rene, her mother — that she had decided her future on the basis of a child's game? It was beyond explanation.

She looked up the mountain. He still wasn't in sight; in fact, there weren't many people coming down the slope, and she began to worry about an accident. Maybe someone had fallen or hit a rock. She imagined all sorts of things that could have happened on the mountainside, and all at once she realized that she was assuming Sam had had an accident. Maybe he had broken his leg or arm, or had had a concussion.

Panic invaded her body. What would her life be like without Sam? She leaned against the small tree near the end of the run. She hadn't thought about that situation. She had only imagined what it would be like to be married to Jason. She had thought about Sam's traveling, but she hadn't explored the idea completely, hadn't gone further than the weekday separations. Life with Sam would be constant fun, constant serendipity as they took each day, never knowing what discoveries it would bring. Small, trivial things gave him joy — for instance, the pull-toy train in the shop. His ability to amuse — that part of his life would be contagious. But was that enough?

While scanning the mountain, she reviewed the reasons she should marry Sam. He was successful in his job, so he certainly had sense. He always saw the bright side of things and was rarely depressed. Not even now, when he wanted something — her — did he succumb to despondency. Yes, he had his downside too. Hadn't she seen the pain in his eyes the night before? But he was able to bounce back and continue fighting for what he wanted. It certainly said something about his disposition!

She wondered if Jason would fight for her and want her as much as Sam did. Or would he accept her decision and not contest it? It was something she would never find out, although someday she would really like to know. But did it matter? The bottom line was that Jason would always be there, would always love her in his own way, and if it wasn't in the same style as Sam — well, that could be compensated for, because they would always be together.

She glanced once more at the mountain, and saw several skiers making their way down, but there was no red parka. Where was he? Had anything happened?

"Dreaming again, Katie?" Sam asked.

He had approached her from behind, and she wanted to shout out, *Thank Goodness! Nothing has happened to you!*

"I waited for you and wondered where you were," she said.

"I went down the far side. It was just something I wanted to do." He took a deep breath. "Something I felt I had to do tonight. Do you understand?"

"I know." She did, really. Magic Mountain had that effect on him too. Funny, they had so much in common, so much that was mystical in their lives, at least here in the shadow of the mountain. It was aptly named. Perhaps others had also discovered its mystery.

They walked toward the lodge as snow fell around them, landing on their hoods and parkas, making the fabric appear blotched before the snow began melting. He held out his hand so that a flake fell onto it, and then he presented the glittering crystal to her. "I can't promise you diamonds," he said simply, and she felt the tears well up in her eyes again. "So this will have to do." He looked at her, and she saw the anguish in his clouded eyes. "Please take this, Katie-Katie," he said, extending his mittened hand to her. "It's all I have to offer you right now. That — and me."

She touched the almost-melted flake and looked up at him. "For tonight," she said, so quietly that he had to strain to hear her. "For tonight, I'll take it." And then she added to herself, *Because I do love you, Sam.*

Chapter Eleven

It wasn't that Katie believed in omens, but while she was getting ready for her last dinner with Sam, her room shook suddenly, and then the picture of Jason and her fell off the dresser, shattering the glass. Was it a sign, she asked herself, a sign that she shouldn't marry Jason? No, that was silly.

She sat on the bed with the broken frame in her hand and looked at the picture. They had been happy then, and she had been content with Jason. Would she be content now? After knowing Sam? The picture was shaking in her hands. She put it down, but her hands continued trembling. She clasped them together, then buried them in the blanket. They had to stop shaking. Sam was waiting for her downstairs and they must not betray her.

She looked in the mirror, and the face that stared back at her was dull, lifeless, as though something terrible had happened. She wiped at her eyes. *Something terrible* has *happened,* she thought. *It's all over. Sam and I . . . tomorrow . . . tomorrow!* No, she wouldn't think about tomorrow.

"Oh, Sam!" she cried out to the empty

room. "If only things were different." Then she smoothed down her dress and straightened her shoulders. She had to look composed and in charge of her emotions. She took another look in the mirror and rubbed at her cheeks, hoping to put some color in her face. She took a deep breath and started to the door. "This is it, Katie, one last night with Sam," she said aloud, wishing that the night would be over quickly and also that it would never end.

She met him in the hall near the dining room. He took her hand and held it, trying to smile, but unable to. Just the way he said it made her want to weep: "Our last night, Katie-Katie. And then it's good-bye."

"Don't, Sam," she said. "Don't talk about it now."

Inside the dining room, she sat in the chair at the window table where they had had their first dinner. It was almost as if he had arranged it purposely. "This is going to be difficult for us," she said.

"We have to talk, Katie. We just can't let this happen. We just can't walk away from each other and do nothing." He moved the vase with a red silk rose to the side of the table. "We have to make one more try to sort this out. I can't lose you like this . . . can't just let you go."

She looked through the window at the mountain. "There are some things you can't undo, Sam. I can't be the kind of woman who will just pick up and go around the world for you. Nor can I be the kind of woman who will sit quietly and wait until you show up on Friday, or once a month. I need more than that. I once told you that the only thing I had in common with my mother was my eyes. I was wrong. I want security, like she wanted it. I need it too."

Sam held her hand and ignored his meal. "There must be some compromises. Life's made up of compromises, Katie."

She shook her head sharply. "Not on this. I just can't see any. Oh, Sam, there doesn't seem to be any answer for us."

"Sometimes we have to create new kinds of answers. Can you honestly say that you don't love me?" He watched the expression on her face, and she knew that he saw her answer. He continued: "Can you truthfully say that you don't want me and that you'd rather marry Jason? That you'll have a better and happier life with Jason? Katie, tell me that you don't love me," he said again. "Go on, say, 'Sam, I don't love you. I love Jason.' "

She shook her head. "You know I can't, don't you? You know —" She stopped, fearing that any sound from her lips would betray her. She heard the band in the next room, the cabaret, begin an old country and western tune, and the lyrics played in her memory. Something about the heartbreak of a woman — the end of a romance, the end of a love — and she wanted to yell to the bandleader to stop playing the song, to stop mocking her. She didn't need words and music to remind her that her heart was breaking.

"I don't like that song," she said.

"Something to recall. When you hear it again, you'll remember me, us, and this night." Sam held her hand tightly, and she kept her wrist rigid, not wanting to move it away from him, wanting him to hold her hand forever.

He looked at their untouched food. "I'm not very hungry," he said.

"Neither am I."

"Let's go somewhere — anywhere." He looked out the window at the few flakes that were coming down from the cloudy sky. "It's snowing again. Probably the last storm of the year."

"No, not outside." She didn't want to be completely alone with him. She knew that he had the power to persuade her to change her mind.

He pushed back his chair and looked down at her. "I want to hold you in my arms, Katie," he said simply. He gestured toward the cabaret. "I've never danced with you. I want to dance with you. I want to hold you in my arms for as long as possible."

They danced through three sets of songs — holding each other tightly, clinging to each other, not speaking, not questioning, just accepting the music and the rhythm and the moment. He held her gently yet firmly, and she wanted to nestle within his arms, dance languidly so that they would always touch. She wanted him to keep his arms around her forever. She had wanted it from their very first moment on the dance floor, when he put his hand on her waist and then on her shoulder.

She put her head on his shoulder, thinking that she was happy here within this protected circle, and wanting the music and the night and the dance to last forever. She heard a woman's laughter from nearby, and then, when a man happily shouted a phrase, the knowledge that other people would enjoy life after this evening filled her with an overwhelming sense of loss and chased away the brief moment of joy. Did the other dancers know that her heart was breaking, that she was saying good-bye to love before she had really ever said hello?

Sam's fingers pressed into her back. "Ah, Katie," he murmured in her ear, "this can't be the end of us. We can't be the characters in some ballad. We're more than that."

He was right, of course. "Tell me what to do, Sam," she quietly cried out to him. "Tell me what to do."

He shook his head. "I wish I could. I could tell you — I could ask you — to come away with me. But that wouldn't be any good. You have to make up your own mind. You're the one who has to decide." He kissed the top of her head. "Because if I tell you, if you don't do it on your own, then we don't have a chance. You might resent me later on, and I'd always wonder if you were happy." He kissed her hair once more. "But know that I do love you."

All around her she could hear the laughter, and the heartrending music flowed through the room, but it was as if it had all been filtered through a curtain, because the sounds were now dull, and only Sam's unhappy voice remained clear. She shuddered and looked up at him. It seemed as though, suddenly, the music overpowered them, and the focus changed, and the curtain lifted so that now she clearly saw his mouth move, and she watched the way his lips were formed as they spoke unheard words of love to her. The way he held her close to him, almost as though they were one, told her more than any heard and spoken pledge ever could that he loved her.

Finally, through the haze of sound, she heard him say quietly, "Let's get out of here."

They walked along the path to Magic Mountain. They were both quiet, and when they heard a distant bell toll eleven times, she kicked weakly at the packed snow, knowing that the day, their last full day, was almost over.

"There's nothing more I can say, Katie. I think — I'm sure that you've made up your mind."

"Yes. I can't help it, Sam. This is all so different, so new. With Jason —" She stopped and began again: "I've never felt quite like this before."

"And you're afraid of it, aren't you?"

She nodded. "My life was so neat and orderly before you came along."

"And that's the way you want it, isn't it?" He picked up a handful of snow and threw it at a tree, turning the dark bark a frosted white. "You know, it all used to be so simple for me too. I would fly from a city without thinking twice. There was nothing to hold me back. But now, every time I move on. . . ."

He left the sentence unfinished, but she knew what he wanted to say. "I can't ask you to change professions, Sam."

"And I wouldn't be happy changing."

There was his truthfulness again. He wouldn't lie even to win her. Which made her wince and love him even more.

They walked silently to the base of the mountain and paused there to observe the skiers at the top. They heard the distant bell strike again.

Sam took her hand and began to lead her back to the lodge. "It's the witching hour, Katie," he said, putting his arm around her.

She heard the last of the twelve rings and he held her apart from him for a moment before he kissed her with gentleness and passion. "Remember me, Katie-Katie. Remember me," he said before letting her go.

She nodded and stood there, pain circling her heart and coursing through her body. "I will, Sam." *How could I ever forget you?* she wanted to cry out, but she remained there mute. She wondered if he could tell that she was hurting inside, that she was wishing all sorts of crazy thoughts, wishing that he would just sweep her away and take her with him. *Convince me, Sam,* she kept crying silently. *Convince me that I shouldn't pay attention to all the should do's and must do's in my life and, just for once, think with my heart. Tell me that I won't make a mistake loving you. Convince me that I can go with you and I can put all*

119

those memories of only weekends with my father behind me. Persuade me that you need me as much as I need you.

Oh, yes, it was true. She loved him, but it seemed so impossible now. *Oh, Sam!* she thought. *I don't know what to do. Help me, Sam, and if not, then, my love, convince me that I don't love you . . . that I'll forget you someday, and this will only be a dream for me to remember on long, cold winter nights.*

Chapter Twelve

Sam was to leave early in the morning, and Katie had told him that she would meet him before breakfast for one last time, but when they parted that last night she knew that she would never see him again. She had lied about their meeting once more.

"In the morning," she had said, and then had taken one long, last look at him as he walked away from her. She remembered calling out his name, and how he had turned around, smiled, and thrown a kiss to her. He had repeated her words, "In the morning," and she had bent her head in agreement. Afterward, as she closed the door to her room, she knew that it was the last time for them. It would be too painful to say good-bye in the morning in front of all those other people. This had been a better and easier way for both of them. There would be no tears for him to see or for her to feel. This was a private grief, and she didn't want to share it with other vacationers in the dining room. No, this was the only way. No use in prolonging the pain. Better to get it over with as soon as possible.

Now she sat in the chair in her room, opposite the small alarm clock on the nightstand. Suddenly it was six and then seven and now nearly eight o'clock. She had been up since early morning. Actually, she hadn't slept, and had only tossed on the bed, recalling and reliving the wonderful moments with Sam throughout the entire week.

It wasn't easy to stay in her room. Her heart told her to go to him, knock on his door, tell him yes, she would go away with him. But her pragmatic side warned her that things could go wrong. She would have no security, and only a part-time husband. In the end, her practical side won, and she remained in her room, picking up and putting down the phone, walking to and from the door.

She could picture Jason in his science lab. Sometimes, on her free period, she would be in the next room, doing her class plans, and she would be able to hear his steady voice explaining the properties of a gas or warning about the effects of certain chemicals on the environment. She would be comforted then, knowing that they would be together. Jason was really a very good person.

But now thoughts of Sam kept getting into her mind. Sam laughing. Sam winding a music box. Sam throwing a snowball. Sam kissing her. When she closed her eyes, it was no use;

Sam's face appeared even in the dark recesses of her mind. *Think, think, think, Katie,* she told herself. *Think of Jason.*

She looked at the clock again. Sam had probably had breakfast, had probably realized that she wasn't coming down. She looked at the telephone. It was odd that he didn't call her. No, it wasn't odd at all. No doubt he knew that she wouldn't be there for breakfast. He knew enough about her and her ways to surmise that that was what she had in mind. But it was curious that he didn't at least try to contact her.

Nine o'clock. He would be getting ready to leave now — the van was to depart for the airport soon. He was taking a ten-o'clock flight to New York, and then he'd be back to the routine of working two weeks overseas and then two in the United States. And everything would be back to the precise way it was long before they had ever met. He would go on with his life, making trips, working with computers, and she would be back in the classroom teaching English.

She walked to the window and looked out at the mountain. Funny, it was the same window she had looked out when she first arrived, in expectation of another wonderful time, another skiing vacation of relaxation and fun. Last week, when she stood here with those happy thoughts, she had had no premonition that someone would enter her life so quickly and change it so radically.

She looked down and saw the maroon guest van in front of the lodge, waiting for the passengers to board. She moved to the side of the window and watched, hoping for a glimpse of Sam. When, finally, he emerged from the lodge, he remained standing there with his luggage, and her heart seemed to leap from her breast. "Sam!" she cried involuntarily, and she was glad he couldn't hear her.

She could see him clearly. He was wearing his red jacket and was hatless. He appeared unhappy and uncertain. He turned around and looked nervously over his shoulder toward the lodge several times. She knew that he was looking for her, searching the groups of people who appeared at the door to the lodge, waiting for her to come. And when the doors of the van opened and the passengers got in, he hesitated and was the last one to enter.

He turned once again at the door and looked up at her window. She stepped back quickly, afraid that he had seen her. But then he swung his luggage onto the rack on the top of the van, climbed inside, and even through her window she heard the muffled thud of the door closing. She saw him look one last time from the side window, and then she watched as the van slowly made its way past the lodge to the main road.

She took a shallow breath. It was finished. Their week was finally over now. There would never be another day of skiing with him . . . another meal to be enjoyed together . . . a time to laugh with each other. Looking down at the empty place where the van had been, she felt a gnawing pain invade her heart, and she clenched her hands. Was this the way it should have ended? Surely some sort of a phrase or even a gesture should have signaled the end. Romances just shouldn't be allowed to die so quietly. She leaned her head onto the cold windowpane, and not knowing how to ritualize the end of a romance, she touched her fingers to her lips and threw a kiss after the van. "To what might have been, my Sam, my wonderful Sam," she murmured.

She stood there until the last moment, following the journey of the van until it disappeared out of sight. She was surprised when she felt teardrops spill over onto her cheeks and then down her face and upon her lips. She hadn't known she was crying.

She wiped at her eyes, but the tears didn't stop. Finally she lay down on her bed and let the tears flow unrestricted. Sam was gone from her life, gone forever. One brief mo-

ment for tears was certainly allowed. This evening she would go home to Maryland, and
there would be no more tears for what might
have been.

Chapter Thirteen

Rene stopped by after the first class. "I don't know about you," she said, "but I had a wonderful time last week. I did nothing but lie on the beach and just listen to the ocean. It was glorious." She held out her arm to show Katie her tan. "No kids to ask questions, no X's and Y's to explain, and no papers to grade. It was marvelous. And what was it like in the snow country?"

Katie frowned. She still hadn't made up her mind whether to tell anyone about Sam. The whole episode — the whole week — was still too confusing for her. It was much too painful for her to speak of him or to even think of him sometimes. Home for two days, she had seen Jason twice, but still hadn't adjusted to the fact that she was Katie Jarvis, English teacher at Southern High, and that at Mountain Laurel she had had a romance with a wonderful, wonderful man. If circumstances had been different, she wouldn't be here, teaching Shakespeare and Swift.

The second-period class was drifting in. "I'll tell you later," she said to Rene. Maybe she'd be able to explain it all so that at least

Rene could understand.

"Uh-oh! That kind of answer usually means it was either so terrible you don't want to talk about it or it was so terrific that it shouldn't be talked about." Rene squinted her eyes. "Which one was it?"

Katie shook her head. "We'll talk later, when there's more time."

"We'll talk at lunch," Rene said.

Later, in the teachers' cafeteria, Katie dawdled with her food as she debated whether to tell Rene about Sam. Why not? Rene was probably the only other person in the world who would understand.

"The one bad thing about getting away from all the kids and teaching is that you have to come back," Rene was saying. "But then again, what else would I do? Don't get me wrong — I really love it here, but there are days I'd rather be somewhere else." She pushed her coffee away. "Okay, Katie, tell me about your vacation. Did you have a good time?"

Katie nodded. "Uh-huh . . . really. All the snow you could ask for, all the skiing under nearly perfect conditions." She tried to keep the conversation light, not wanting to reveal anything. Maybe by the time she was ready to talk about it, all the hurt would have disappeared.

Rene cocked her head to one side. "Is that all? You've gone away before and have never come back quite like this." She stared at Katie. "No, there's something about you, something different. Something happened there, didn't it? I can tell. There's something that I can't quite figure out . . . something that's happy and yet sad with you. If I didn't know you better, Katie, I would say you met someone." She narrowed her eyes. "You did, didn't you? I knew it. I just knew it! It's in your eyes."

Katie took a deep breath. "I always said you were my best friend. You're right. I did meet someone at the lodge, but it's not like you think." *Not like I want to think, either,* she thought, and then she remembered Sam's smile and slightly crooked tooth, and for a moment she could almost believe that she was back at the lodge, waiting for him to ski down the mountain with her.

"Want to talk about him?"

"Maybe I should, just to figure out some things. To put it all in perspective." She toyed with her tablespoon. Where should she begin? "Sam — that's his name — was at the lodge too, and I met him on the slopes." She leaned across the table, intending to keep her voice low, so that no one could overhear.

"Hello," a hearty voice said. "You two look like you're conspiring against the principal."

Katie and Rene looked up as Jason put a tray of food on the table and sat down. "Whew! These kids are always difficult the first day back." He smiled at the two women. "I figure this is a wasted day."

"Yeah," Rene agreed. "Katie and I were just comparing notes about classes. I think we all hate getting back to our routines."

Jason unwrapped his food. "Yes, but sometimes it's not too bad. At least you know what you're going to be doing for the next few weeks."

Jason was right, Katie thought. Routine is not really too bad if you like what you're doing and whom you're doing it with. She watched as he ate his cheese sandwich. She had always liked routine too. It was nice and secure. But now — now she felt a strange stirring deep within her. She felt as though she were being confined.

She shook her head. That was silly. No one was telling her what to do. This was the life she had chosen. This was the life she was used to and had been happy with for these past years. This was what she enjoyed. She knew that from every Monday to Friday she would have lunch in this cafeteria with Rene and Jason, and she could even count on the fact that Jason would have a cheese sandwich and a glass of milk, and that there would be spaghetti on Tuesdays, and that the lunch menus would alternate every week except on special holidays. No, there really wasn't anything wrong with routine. It was what made her feel safe.

Then why did she feel that she wanted to run away? She had never felt this way before. She looked through the window and saw the sunshine and the trees, which were beginning to leaf. She knew that she should be happy — spring had finally arrived. But there was this ache in her chest near her heart, and it wouldn't go away.

She took a sip of her coffee. Maybe it was just too recent — the vacation and the fun . . . and Sam. Maybe, probably, she would forget all about Mountain Laurel. Maybe all the fun and good times would fade and Sam would become just another memory. But she didn't want to forget, and that was the problem. She didn't want to forget about last week or Mountain Laurel . . . or about Sam.

"Hey, see you this evening?" Jason touched her hand very quickly, and she started.

"What?"

"You see, Rene, she doesn't want to be here, either." He touched Katie's hand again. "I said that I'll see you this evening."

"Yes, this evening." She looked at the clock on the wall. "I've got to get back to class."

The rest of the day went by quickly. Jason was right. The students wanted to talk about their vacation, but she stuck to her role as teacher, and after assigning two poems for homework, she gave them the chance to put down their vacation happenings on paper. When the bell rang, she collected the essays, promising to read the best ones aloud the following day. At least, she reasoned, it was a way of getting them to think and write.

She looked around the empty classroom and focused on a beam of sunshine that filtered in through the window so that she could see bits of chalk dust floating in the air. It was really nice being here. She liked the quiet at the end of the day, and she even liked the smell of the erasers. But it would never be the same again. There would always be a lingering doubt about whether she had made the correct choice, sort of like in Francis Stockton's short story, "The Lady or the Tiger?".

She stacked all the essays and glanced at a poster on the far wall; it depicted a skier poised to go downhill. Last year's senior class had given it to her when they graduated — "just to remember us by," they told her when she walked into the room and saw it hanging. While she stared at it, suddenly the skier became Sam and once again she heard his shout of "Katie . . . Katie!" She took a deep breath.

Getting over Sam would be difficult. But she would have to; Sam was a roamer and would always be one. Not like Jason . . . good, steady Jason. And it wasn't as though she wasn't fond of him. After all, she was engaged to him. She pushed her chair away from her desk and put her head down, feeling guilty. What would Jason say if he knew her thoughts?

Rene opened the door and closed it quickly. "Need a shoulder to cry on?" she asked.

Katie nodded. "Yeah. Can I use yours?"

"Anytime." She sat down on the desk beside Katie. "Tell me about Sam."

"He was there on vacation, like me. And he was alone . . ." Katie began.

Nodding her head from time to time, Rene listened as Katie told of the way she and Sam had met and of the time they spent together.

"And that's all there was to it?" Rene asked afterward.

"Wasn't that enough?"

"Well, you've told me all about your week with Sam and what a great time you had, but you forgot to tell me one important thing."

"What's that?"

"You didn't tell me how you feel about him now. You told me all the highlights, but you never said what you really feel about him. And I think that's the problem, isn't it?"

"I don't know how to answer that."

"Truthfully!"

"I can't. I don't know. . . ."

"Maybe you don't want to know."

Katie lowered her head. "No. Yes. Oh, Rene! It all seemed so perfect — meeting Sam, being with him and doing all sorts of wonderful things that I've always wanted to do. But then this coming back to reality. . . ." She slumped back into her chair.

"It was tough, wasn't it?"

Katie sighed. "But maybe I'm worried for nothing." She watched as the chalk dust played within the shaft of light. "Sam's probably one of those love-them-and-leave-them guys." She touched her friend's arm. "Instead of a summer romance, maybe this is only a winter fascination." She smiled sadly. "Variation on an old theme. Maybe it'll all pass in another week." She tried to laugh but didn't quite succeed.

Rene played with the writing extension of the desk. "You don't really believe that, do you? I thought you said he was a nice guy."

"Yes, but nice guys can speak a good line too. Can't they?"

"Don't do that, Katie. Don't try to joke it away. I can tell you're hurting." Rene drummed her fingers against the top of the desk. "It seems to me that you have a very

134

real problem, my friend. And I just don't mean Sam Whoever."

Katie looked at her, puzzled. "But I won't hear from him again, Rene. I told him never to call."

"That's not quite all the problem, Katie. Even if he never calls you — and I'm not so sure that will happen — you're going to have to think about your relationship with Jason." Rene got up and walked over to the skiing poster. "Seems to me that your meeting this Sam was an omen. Maybe you really shouldn't marry Jason. Maybe that's part of your problem. You're doing something you don't want to do."

Katie shook her head. "Don't say that. My whole life for the past year has been geared toward marrying him. I never said I loved him — not honest-to-goodness real love — but Jason and I understand each other. I think we'd be good for each other. And that's another kind of love."

"You're kidding yourself." Rene picked up a piece of chalk and started to write on the blackboard. "One, Jason . . . two, Sam . . . three, Katie." She drew a triangle and smiled. "Hey, I can't help it if I'm the consummate geometry teacher." She joined the three lines of the triangle with the names in each corner. "No matter how you figure it, Katie, X and

135

Y and Z don't a marriage make." She drew a slash through the entire triangle. "I think you'd better get your feelings in order."

Katie nodded, knowing that her friend was right. But what was she to do? Why tell Jason and hurt him if Sam was never coming back to her? She could still go on and marry Jason, still be a good wife to him. She would make him happy — and he would never know.

Chapter Fourteen

Katie watched as Jason finished coaching the baseball team. He was wearing the Baltimore Orioles cap that she had given him for a birthday present. His lucky cap, he called it, because last year's team had gotten to the semifinals in the state championship.

"Hi." Jason tossed her a ball. "I'll be right there. Shall we get something to eat?" He turned away to speak to a player. Jason was always speaking to someone, always willing to give of his time, especially to her. Whenever she had to do something, whether to coach the cheerleaders or help with the class play, Jason was always ready to help too. No wonder everyone liked him. It was as though he could do no wrong.

And she? She constantly felt guilty. Here she was, keeping the lie about Sam within her. But was it actually a lie? Nothing had really happened. She realized that she had been doing that a lot lately, denying that anything had happened at Mountain Laurel. If she repeated it often enough, maybe it would become the truth.

★ ★ ★

137

"Hey, Katie," Jason said as they sat in her apartment that evening. "You never did tell me about your vacation. But then, it's probably because I've gone on so much about the team." He held her hand. "Sorry, I get carried away sometimes."

She glanced down at their hands. Maybe now was a good time to tell him. She would chat about the whole week in a slow, casual voice and not make a big deal out of it.

"Okay, tell me. I promise to listen." Jason settled back against the cushions.

She shrugged. "Oh, it was like always — good skiing, lots of people. I even met someone who teamed up with me on the slopes." There, she'd begun to tell him. She looked up to see if his face indicated that he suspected anything amiss. But no, he was watching her with the interest he always showed in her skiing trips.

"From around here?"

"What?"

"Was the person from around here or the North or where?"

"From the Midwest. Actually, he works overseas. It was sort of a minivacation for him too." She touched one of the music boxes. Maybe if she and Jason went to Mountain Laurel, she would be able to find out if it was just the setting or if she had really fallen in

138

love with Sam. Perhaps, if she and Jason were there together, she'd find out the truth. "Come with me to Mountain Laurel for a weekend before it gets too warm," she urged him. "Just once."

He finished his coffee. "Not me, Katie. You know I'm not a winter person. I guess that's one of the few things we'll never agree on." He shook his head. "Sometimes I don't think I'll ever understand you and how you like chasing the last of the snow, especially when everyone else is waiting for the sun and the warm weather. It must be some instinctive thing with you, something you've always wanted or had when you were a little girl."

She tried to make him see what she saw when she was there. "It's the peace," she said. "Everything is blanketed. You're cold, but inside you're warm because you're content." How could she ever explain it to him? It was something you had to experience, the special feeling that you were the only person in the world. She wanted to tell him about the beauty and grandeur of the snow-covered mountains and the impression it made on her, but he continued to shake his head.

"If you say so, Katie. To each her own." He reached for her, and she offered no resistance as he held her in his arms. "I hope you don't think you're ever going to reform me. I'll tell you what. Promise me that, after we're married, you won't try to reform me and turn me into a snow person, and I'll promise not to insist that you like the hot weather." He laughed. "Let's never try to change each other. After all, I like you just the way you are." He kissed her gently on the lips. "I really do, Katie."

She leaned her head back into the cushions. Maybe his kisses weren't as exciting as Sam's, but they were genuine, and that only made her feel more depressed. If only there was something not to like about Jason — but of course there wasn't. He was much too nice.

He kissed her once again and left, and she felt a pang of deceit. He had never asked any other questions about Sam, not even his name. That was because he trusted her. How was he to know that Sam had come into her life and changed all the rules?

She opened the book of poetry where she had put Sam's picture and took it out. She had forgotten about the photo until this morning, when she was searching for a certain poem by Langston Hughes and it fell out. She held the picture in front of her and looked at it, remembering the time when it was taken. They were standing near the top of Magic Mountain and another skier had come by and asked them if they would take his picture.

After they did, as thanks, he took one of them.

It was her only picture of him, but she knew that she didn't need, nor would she ever need, the actual photograph in front of her to remember him. He was there in her memory. She smiled to herself as she remembered that one of her first impressions of him was that his ears were just a bit too large for his face but that they somehow gave him an endearing quality. No, she didn't need a photograph. He was indelibly captured in her mind.

She looked at the phone on the table. Sometimes, when it was late at night and she couldn't sleep, she would imagine that the phone had rung, and when she answered it, it would be Sam calling from some distant place, and they would talk for hours about what they were doing and what they would do. But then she'd fall asleep, and even though many of her dreams were punctuated with glimpses of him, he would be so far away that she could never get to him.

Once she had dreamed that they were still at Mountain Laurel. She was at the top of Devil's Mist and Sam was waiting for her at the bottom of the run. Somehow, everything that was vital to them depended on her getting down the slope. She could even hear Sam saying, "Come, Katie, come on. Follow me, we'll do this together." But she stood there paralyzed. And then she woke up and realized that she had called his name. She stared into the dark until she realized that it was only a dream, a nightmare, and there was no Sam to meet and no Devil's Mist to conquer. She had tried to go back to sleep then, but, instead, tossed on her bed for the remaining two hours before her alarm clock went off.

Tonight was another night like that one; only, this time someone had phoned her and then hung up before she could answer. It had awakened her, and she lay there, her arm outstretched toward the phone, waiting for it to ring again, fantasizing that it was Sam calling her. When she awoke the next morning, her arm was numb.

"If I tell you you look terrible, believe me," Rene told Katie in the parking lot that morning. "It must be your conscience." As Katie opened her mouth to speak, Rene caught herself: "I'm sorry. Just an unfortunate use of words." She locked her car door. "Still haven't heard from him?"

"I really don't expect to." Katie shifted the stack of folders in her arms. "I told you it's all over."

"Only if you want it to be." Rene opened the door to the school building. "I keep telling you — go for it. Tell Jason the wedding's off. Call Sam and tell him the wedding's on. A plus B equals C. Mathematically proven." She smiled.

"You make everything seem so simple."

"Because that's the way it should be."

"I can't do it, Rene. I can't trade my life."

"Your orderly, well-tuned life?"

"Suppose Sam was just a flight of fancy, that he really had no lasting effect?"

"Then you would have known it by now." Rene stopped at the foot of the hall stairs. "Tell me truthfully — have you forgotten about Sam?" She peered at her friend. "You don't even have to answer that — your face tells me my answer." She started running up the stairs, leaving Katie behind. "I'm telling you, my friend, go for it." She turned at the landing and swept her arms out to include the schoolrooms and the hall and stairs. "There are other schools, other places. But is there another Sam Hubbard for you? Answer that riddle, Katie, and then you'll know what to do." Rene disappeared down a hall.

Katie had assigned an essay on romantic poetry, and she knew that most students would choose to analyze one of Elizabeth Barrett Browning's sonnets, and quote the famous lines, "How do I love thee? Let me count the ways." She could see and hear them now, reading it aloud, snickering, circulating notes with parodies.

She remembered the first time she had heard the words and been stirred by their pledge of eternal devotion. Fifteen and ingenuous, she had asked herself then if she could ever love anyone that deeply or that strongly. Today she knew the answer.

Chapter Fifteen

Katie stayed after school to talk to two students who needed more guidance in their work. She had tried to show the difference between fact and fiction in a book report, and the two boys wanted a more thorough explanation.

"Well," Katie said, "if you know something to be true and you write it, that's fact. But if you're not sure and you make up something, even just one sentence about it, that's fiction." She turned to wave at Rene, who had taken a seat in the classroom. "But that doesn't mean that fiction can't turn to fact. It can." She smiled at the boys. "Okay? It's that simple."

When the students had left and they were alone in the classroom, Rene said, "For someone who can teach an English course on what's fact and what's fiction, you sure do a lousy job of mixing it up in real life."

"Please, let's not start on Jason and me again."

"Let's not forget Sam. You do remember Sam, don't you? The guy you met at Mountain Laurel, the guy you fell in love with?" Rene took out a pencil and tapped it. "That's fact,

Katie," she said, mimicking her friend's words. "It's that simple."

Katie nodded. "I know. But what about the other part — the fiction? I haven't heard from him, not since he left."

"You told him not to bother you, that it couldn't be."

"But he really hasn't tried to contact me . . . not in three weeks."

"Maybe he will yet. But that's not the entire problem. Even if you never hear from him again," Rene persisted, "you're still going to have to do something about Jason. You don't love him and never will. Sam proved it. It's not fair to Jason."

"We could have a good marriage," Katie said weakly.

"Great! And you'd settle for it?" Rene walked to the blackboard and idly drew circles on it. "Don't you want something more, Katie? You just don't fall in love with a man within two or three days and then say, 'The heck with it, I'm going back to my nice, little, safe corner of the world.' "

Katie stared at her friend. That was exactly what Sam had said to her — that she would rather take second-best, that she'd rather not go for the gold. That was why she didn't attempt Devil's Mist after that first time — it was too frightening. Better to be safe than sorry, and now here she was — safe *and* sorry. Jason was here and she was going to marry him, and Sam was elsewhere and she was in love with him.

"Jason and I want the same things. We have the same values."

"And you're both schoolteachers and you both understand your professions and you would both stay right here on this spot of earth for the rest of your lives. Is that what you want?"

"You make it sound so dull, so boring."

"It is, Katie. There's no life there. You just think you want the same things because you saw how unhappy your mother was with your father's job. But did you ever think that it might have been more, that his traveling was only a cover-up, that maybe there was something basically wrong with the marriage and that travel was the handiest excuse around? Maybe, if you asked your mother for the real reason, you would learn something about her and your father.

"Katie, you can't try to live your life by reliving your mother's. You can't save the world or change it. It just is, and believe me, you have to go out and do the best you know how . . . love whomever you want. You owe yourself that much. I saw you when you came home from the ski trip. There was a sparkle in your eyes, a happiness I hadn't seen since you were a kid. You were alive again, emotionally and mentally. And it was all because you'd met Sam." She drew a small circle on the board and then placed points around the orbit. "This circle is you and Jason," she said, writing in their names. And then she pointed to a distant dot. "And this is Sam."

"Floating all around the earth, I notice." Katie laughed even though she knew it was true and it hurt her.

"At least he's able to get a better perspective on the world." Rene drew a line from the dot to Katie's name within the circle. "This is your way out of a nice little niche that you've created. And if I were you, I'd think very carefully about it."

Everything Rene had said was true. She would be locked into a predictable and prosaic life with Jason, and she wondered why neither of them ever talked about transferring to another school or district, or even moving to another town. Surely Jason would be at least an assistant principal if not a principal in another school. He was capable and had a good rapport with students.

But then again, so was she, and she hadn't considered transferring. Maybe Rene was right, maybe she had settled down at an early age. She was only in her twenties. Why hadn't she done anything about her career? She was a good teacher and could be an assistant principal, but the thought had never entered her mind. Rene was right — she didn't have any ambition. And neither did Jason. They were too content and secure to move on. She wondered if they had done that to each other.

"Are you listening, Katie?" Rene's words cut through her reverie. "If I were you I'd talk to Jason, tell him what's been going on, make him see that you two aren't good for each other because you don't love him. It's that simple. Tell him the honest truth." Picking up the chalk again, she wrote Sam's name on the board once more. "And then I would write Sam a letter. Or I would call him and tell him what you've done and that maybe he should come visit you. And then — well, then you will see what happens." She folded her hands as though she had just completed a lesson. "Any discussion?"

"And if I can't locate him?"

"You can."

"And if he doesn't want me?"

"Ah," Rene said, "that's the key question. Well, if he doesn't want you, he won't answer. And if he doesn't answer, then you won't have to deal with whether you should marry him. And if you don't deal with it, you will have at least cleared up the Jason-and-you match."

She erased the blackboard. "Oh, Katie! Don't be as stupid as I was once upon a time."

Katie shook her head. "I don't understand."

Rene sat down at a desk and pursed her lips.

"I've been wondering whether I should tell you this." She looked away through the window toward the white dogwoods in bloom at the front of the school. "Don't ask me any questions, and don't ask me when this all happened. Just sit and listen, and when I'm finished, just file it under 'gone but not forgotten' and never talk to me about it again. You'll understand why." She took a deep breath.

"A few years ago, when I went away on one of my beach weekends, I met someone I considered pretty special. It was summer, we were both on vacation, and one thing led to another and there I was, head over heels in love with this guy. I won't even tell you his name — not that I've forgotten it. I never will, Katie, but his name is important only to me. Like your Sam, he was totally different from me, and he absolutely swept me off my feet and I loved it. But to make this very long and very sad story very brief, he was going back to his hometown somewhere in the Northeast, and when he asked me to go too, I thought about everything I had — my family, friends, career — and I said I couldn't do it.

It wasn't that I needed those roots — I knew they would always be there for me — but he was so absolutely different from me, and I was, to put it quite simply, afraid to take the chance. I was too darn scared to go with him."

Rene shook her head. "That was several years ago, and I've never forgotten him. I never heard from him again, and when I came home I never said anything to anyone. I think that was because I knew immediately, even while driving home from the beach, that I had made a mistake. But a lot of things — pride, stupidity, fear — never allowed me to write or call him. And now I look back and say to myself that it was so foolish of me . . . so very foolish."

Rene looked once more at the dogwoods. "And I don't want that to happen to you, my friend." She stood up and grabbed her purse. "Learn from other people's mistakes, Ms. Jarvis! I lost a love because I was too demanding and set in my mind. Go for it, Katie! Go for it!"

Katie opened her mouth to speak, but Rene motioned her to silence. "Uh-uh. I told you — no questions . . . ever. What's done is done! So come on, I've got a ton of papers to grade this evening though maybe I'll just forget them and read a book. I'll give the papers back next week." Rene laughed. "Only those who passed the test will be interested in their marks. Somehow, the kids who don't know a right triangle from a circle couldn't care less."

Chapter Sixteen

When she saw the postman put the letters into the mailboxes, Katie knew somehow that there would be a letter from Sam. She saw it immediately, the plain white envelope with the no-nonsense, almost-print handwriting, and she peered at the return address from somewhere in England. Her hand trembled as she tore it open, and a thousand thoughts raced through her mind as she read the letter.

My dearest Katie,

I hope this is welcome news. I'm afraid I can't keep my promise to you, the one that I agreed to when I told you I would never try to contact you. I'm afraid, my love, it is much too difficult and too high a price to pay in my life right now. I won't bore you with the details — let it be sufficient to say that I'm traveling, doing well, and, Katie-Katie, I miss you very much.

Maybe you've had a chance to think about us and have been able to sort out the obstacles that keep us apart. Doesn't that sound so terribly old-fashioned?

Katie, I will be in the States next week

*and I will call you. Maybe it's not too late
for us!*

> *Know that I love you very much,*
> *Sam*

She held the letter tightly and reread it, almost hearing him speak the words. Then she looked at the postmark. Last week! That meant he was going to telephone any day now.

She sat down at the kitchen table. Was it welcome news? If she had to tell the truth, yes, it was — very welcome although she knew that seeing him again would only cloud her plans. Her heart was racing. Yes, she did want to see him, there was no question about that. She missed him and his easy humor, and the excitement of being with him.

She sighed. Should she tell Rene? Should she allow him to visit? There were so many questions now that she knew that she was totally in love with Sam. But first, she had to think about Jason. She owed him so much. And she owed him the courtesy of telling him about Sam. Even if she and Sam never lived happily ever after as in fairy tales, she knew that she couldn't go through with the marriage to Jason. That was finished. In fact, it was finished when Sam kissed her on the farmhouse steps.

She reached for the phone; she should tell

Jason immediately. She started to dial, and then replaced the receiver. No, that would be cowardly and mean, and she owed Jason more than that. She had to face him and explain what was happening.

Once more she picked up the phone, and once more she put it down. If she called Jason and asked him to meet her, he would think something was wrong with her, and he would probably rush over to her apartment. And she didn't want that. She wanted to tell him about her and Sam in a public place, though not in school, where there would be too many interruptions by students and faculty members. And certainly not in the school cafeteria.

She would wait until they went to The Country Cottage tomorrow night. *Then* she would tell him. They would have privacy, but it was open enough so that she wouldn't cry when she told him.

It was sad. She never liked to hurt anyone, and here she was hurting someone who had once figured to be a big part of her life. Endings, even of sad movies, always made her cry. It was silly, but that was the way she was in spite of her strong ideas of how people should behave. Crying was necessary sometimes.

Okay, tomorrow she would talk with Jason and tell him that she was breaking off their engagement, that someone else had come into her life. She put her head down. It was terrible — it was so cruel. But as Rene had once told her, "You sometimes have to be cruel. There's no other way. Are you going to marry him just because you feel sorry for him?" Rene was right. Better to get it over with quickly, once and for all, and then plan the next step no matter what it was.

And the next step — what was that to be? It was still a huge hurdle — she just wouldn't be comfortable with Sam away so often. It wouldn't be enough for her. She needed companionship and love and a sense of being needed. With Sam, she wouldn't be sure that he needed her. He was so self-sufficient.

She read the letter for a third time and then replaced it in its envelope. First she must meet Jason, because no matter what happened between her and Sam, she knew that she could never marry Jason. She admitted it. She didn't love him. She really never had. Sam was right — she had settled for something other than love, and it was fine as long as she hadn't experienced the feeling of genuine happiness. But now that Sam had come into her life, she'd begun to cherish the experience of being loved and loving.

She would talk with Jason tomorrow, and then figure out what to do about Sam.

Chapter Seventeen

While the waitress took their orders, Katie wondered how she could tell Jason that she wanted to break their engagement. How would he take it? She wanted to grasp his arm and cry, "Jason, say something! Make me think that I'm wrong, that I really do love you and we really should marry." But Jason was silent. He had no reason to know what she was thinking and no reason to suspect what was about to be said. In his mind, he and Katie were set — set for life. Only Katie knew that that assumption was wrong.

She sighed. No use putting it off. Maybe if she waited until they were back in her apartment . . . maybe then she could speak easier. But she knew it was really only another excuse not to talk to Jason about the situation.

"Something's on your mind, Katie." Jason snapped his fingers in front of her face, the way he always did when she had that faraway look in her eyes and he wanted to bring her back to earth. He said, "What's troubling you? You've been extra quiet all evening — all day, in fact." He smiled at her. "You've been quiet all week. Something's wrong, isn't it?"

"Oh, Jason," Katie began, "I don't know how I can tell you this." She circled the rim of her water glass with her finger.

"Why don't you just say it, Katie?"

She took a deep breath. "Because I don't want to hurt you." He seemed startled by her words and she realized that he had no idea what she was talking about. "Jason, it's us." How could she tell him the rest of it when he looked at her as though she were speaking a language he didn't understand? But she had to, and she took a deep breath. "I can't marry you, Jason," she finally blurted out, angry that they weren't the words she had wanted to use. "I'm not sure of you . . . of us." She bunched up her napkin. "No, that's not true. I'm not sure of me." She looked at him briefly. "It's me. I'm the problem."

"Want to talk about it?" He reached for her hand, but she pulled it away, then was immediately sorry she did it. The action — the rejection — had hurt him. She could tell by the way his eyes had clouded for a second. And he seemed confused. "Is it something I've done?"

She shook her head. "No."

"Is it something I should have done?" He smiled, and she knew it was his attempt at humor, and she hated herself for hurting him.

"No." She looked down at the table while

the waitress served their coffee. "It's something *I've* done. It's my problem, not yours."
She wanted him to know that he really didn't play a part in her decision, that he was truly the innocent party, that whatever had happened was because of her and Sam.

"It's that man you met at Mountain Laurel, isn't it? The man you skied with at the lodge."

She nodded her head, miserable that she was hurting him and yet surprised that he remembered their conversation and could piece it all together. She'd thought that he hadn't been listening, or even been concerned when she told him about Sam. "Yes, it's Sam. I wish you had really listened to me when I told you about him, when I first met him."

"I thought I had, because I remembered him. I guess I wasn't listening to it all, though." He blinked his eyes in confusion, and her heart went out to him. "I thought it was, at most, just a — a —"

"A flirtation?" she asked gently. "A winter romance?" When he nodded, she bit her lip. "I thought so too, but it wasn't. It hasn't turned out that way."

"I was sure —" he began, and then stopped, waited a few seconds, and began again: "I was sure that it was just something you had to get over, that you needed the . . . the — what shall I call it? — I'll use your word — the flirtation. I thought you needed the excitement of. . . ." He looked at his hands. "Well, never mind." He sipped his coffee. "You don't love me now, do you?"

Katie's stomach was a huge knot. No matter what anyone said, breaking up wasn't easy. She didn't want to hurt Jason, but she had to. She had to tell him how she felt.

"Jason, it's not that I don't love you now. It's probably that I never really loved you. If I'm honest and fair, I have to take the whole blame. You haven't changed. I have. You're still you. Only, I'm not the same Katie Jarvis. You represented everything I wanted. You're a fine and really wonderful man, but I don't love you. I guess I always knew it, but it was easier not to acknowledge it. You were what I would have wanted if I had to make up a list of all the good qualities in a husband. But, Jason, what's missing is. . . ." How could she explain it more clearly?

He said it for her: "The spark?"

"Yes, the spark."

He stirred his coffee, swirling it around and around. "I know I've never been the most exuberant or the most exciting person in the world. In fact, I guess I'm a pretty dull person."

She shook her head. "No . . . no."

"There's no denying it, Katie. Like you,

160

I am what I am."

She closed her eyes. Sam had said something like that too: *"What you see is what you get, Katie."*

"You're away again, Katie, dreaming of other things. . . ." Jason waited until the waitress had put the check on the table. "The spark — does he have it?" he asked.

She nodded. "Yes." How she wished she could run away right now, end the conversation, end this terrible meeting.

He looked off at the waitress, who was at another table. "Are you going to marry him?"

She shrugged. "I don't know," she said "Right now I don't think so. It's very complicated."

"Does he love you?"

His voice was flat, and she knew the extent of his pain. He would never have asked these questions before. No, Jason never probed too deeply for answers. Life had always been easy and good for him. Complications weren't for him. He had a scientific mind, and if something went wrong, he could always work it out logically. Everything had a cause and effect. That was one of his favorite sayings, and now even she could apply it to this situation. The cause was Sam and the effect was that she couldn't marry Jason. How simple it all seemed when she worked it out analytically.

How simple and how cold.

"Please don't ask me anything else," she said. "I can't answer." She touched his arm. "I wish that this had never happened." She stood up. "I'm sorry. I'm really sorry. You're nice and you're kind and you're a good teacher and a fine person and. . . ."

"But that's not enough, is it, Katie?" Again she shook her head, and he reached for her hand once more. "Will you sit down for just a few more minutes and hear me out?"

She couldn't refuse the request. She owed him that much, at least. He had been more than decent, and she knew if the situation were reversed, she'd be hurt and furious, angry and mean. But Jason wasn't like that. He could never be mean to anyone. Oh, why did this happen? Why did she go to Mountain Laurel? Why did she meet Sam? Why did she fall in love with him? There were too many questions to be asked and answered. She sat down again.

Jason moved his finger around the table. "You know, Katie, when we first started going out together, I thought you were the finest person in the world and I was really happy that you and I got along so well. And then, when everything kept going along so smoothly, I just naturally thought we should marry." He wrinkled his brow. "Oh, it wasn't that I took you for granted. I just assumed, you see, that we would get married. That's how it's been in my life — a lot of assumptions." He smiled at her, and if there was any way she could have erased Sam at that moment, she would have. But she couldn't, and she and Jason both knew it.

"You've sort of stunned me, Katie, because, you see, I've never even considered what we were doing, either. It was like I was on a track, and you were on the track next to me, and we both sort of merged somewhere along the way." He held up his hand. "Oh, not that I don't love you — please don't think that. I do, but it was something I just took for granted. Katie and Jason, Jason and Katie. Maybe I should have thought, 'Katie loves Jason, Jason loves Katie.' Maybe I wasn't romantic enough. Maybe that's where I went wrong."

"No, you didn't go wrong. I did." She wanted to make him know that nothing could have changed what had happened.

He took a sip of his coffee. "Well, that doesn't seem to matter now, does it?" He smiled. "But you're right about one thing — I didn't listen to you carefully. Maybe it was because we just drifted into this arangement . . . this relationship. It was as if nothing better came along to interfere with us. So maybe we both just figured, 'Well, why not marry?' " He picked up the check and folded it. "But something better has now come along, Katie — for you, not for me — and I don't want to hold you back. I won't hold you back. I could never hurt you, Katie, or wish you harm."

She looked at him and could feel her lower lip tremble. "I'm sorry."

"I think you're right. I think that's all we are — just friends." He took out his wallet. "Maybe I should have let you pay your half all these months. It might have helped our relationship."

She knew it was another attempt at humor, and she said through the lump in her throat, "Jason — dear, wonderful, kind Jason. I wish . . . I know you'll find someone who will really love you and appreciate how nice you really are."

He drove her to her apartment, and she knew it was for the last time. She felt saddened that their engagement was over. Jason was reliable and kind and decent, and she would never forget him — just as she would never forget Sam, even if she never saw him again. This was his legacy to her — she had come to know love and to have it play an important part in her life. She could never settle for anything less.

"You won't change your mind?" Jason

asked her as he turned the ignition key off.

When she shook her head, he leaned over and kissed her lightly on her cheek. "Okay, Katie. Never let it be said that I don't know when to give up." He reached across and opened her door. "I won't come in — I have a lot to think about tonight." He touched her cheek again. "I'll see you at school."

Chapter Eighteen

A postcard arrived from Italy the next day. Sam's handwriting was small and his message was rambling, as though he didn't know which subjects would interest her. He ended: *Working my way home — be there in two weeks. Don't make any plans until then. You must see the snow and the skiing. It makes Devil's Mist look small. Will talk to you in a few days. All my love, S.*

The other side was a tourist's view of the Alps, and he had circled one of the smaller mountains, labeling it *Devil's Mist.*

She shuddered, but didn't know whether it was from anticipation at seeing him or the recollection of Devil's Mist and her inability to conquer it. Probably a little of both. "All my love," he had written, and she knew that he meant it.

She propped the card up on her dresser so that the picture was in full view. Then she crossed to the window and looked out at the darkness. The weatherman had promised a mild spring day, but the evening air had turned cold. Despite the temperature, she knew that it was already the end of winter.

The snow would be thawing at Mountain Laurel by now, and there would be no more trips there until next year. She was sorry about that; she would have liked going back to see the farmhouse and the inn. Even Devil's Mist seemed appealing now. In fact, everything about the lodge appealed to her at this moment, and she knew that it was because of all the sweet memories associated with it. Magic Mountain would never be the same . . . nor would she. The ghost of Sam would always be there.

She took another look at the postcard before turning off the light. One problem — Jason — solved and another — Sam — to begin soon. She'd think about him tomorrow, when she was rested and less vulnerable, when she could make intelligent decisions. For now, though, she was mentally and physically tired and all she wanted to do was sleep.

The ringing phone awoke her. "Hello," she said, still hazy from her deep sleep.

"*La Signorina Jarvis, per favore* . . . please." The Italian operator's voice startled her and she was instantly awake.

"Yes." She grasped the telephone tighter and took a deep breath, afraid to move, as though by breathing she would banish the dream. But it was real and she knew it, and she also knew that Sam was calling. She waited while the operator spoke to someone first in the foreign language and then in English. After what seemed several minutes she heard him at last.

"Katie? Katie, it's Sam." His voice was exactly as she remembered it — deep, smooth, and yet a bit excited.

"I know." She paused, waiting for him to say something while her mind raced ahead, wanting to ask him dozens of questions, wanting to tell him hundreds of things.

"Katie? I can hardly hear you."

"I . . . I didn't say anything. Sam, where are you?" That was an inane thing for her to ask. She knew he was in Italy.

"I wrote twice."

"I got your letter. Your card came today." She shook her head. What foolish things people say when they speak long distance. *Talk to me, Sam,* she wanted to cry. *Tell me why you called me in the middle of the night.*

His voice was hesitant. "I had so much . . ." he began, and then stopped and started over again. "I wanted to talk to you. Katie, I've missed you. This won't work. I've done nothing but think about you."

"Yes." She licked her parched lips. "I know."

"We've got to talk and come to some sort of resolution. Good-bye isn't for us. There has to be more."

She heard static, and was afraid that they had been disconnected. "Sam?" She shouted.

"I'm here, Katie. Look, I have to ask you this. Can I come to see you when I get back?"

"Yes."

"Good. That's what I was hoping. I'll be there in another week. Promise me you won't do anything foolish till I get there and we talk about things."

"I won't." Did he suspect that she would be counting the days?

"Are you all right?"

"Yes. And you?" Such polite conversation, she thought. Surely they had more important things to say.

"Yes."

They were both silent. Is this all they had to talk about? *Sam*, she wanted to say, *a lot has happened to me. I have so much to tell you.* But she said nothing.

"I just had this crazy notion that I should call you, Katie-Katie. I know it's late and you have to teach but. . . ."

"Don't apologize, Sam. I'm glad you called. I would have answered your letter, but I didn't have an address."

"I've been moving around a lot these past weeks." His tone became more serious: "Katie, think about me — think about us."

"I am . . . I do."

"I miss you very much. I love you, Katie." He said the words so quietly that she had to strain to hear them.

Yes, she wanted to answer him. *I know, and I love you too.* Instead, she listened.

"In one week . . . I'll be there in another week."

"I'll wait for you, Sam."

"That's all I ask, Katie. . . ."

She heard the click of his phone, and then put down her own. She wished that she had told him about her breaking off with Jason.

She sat back against her pillows and pulled the blanket around her. It was three o'clock, and it would be another sleepless night for her.

As she recalled the conversation, a wave of yearning washed over her. How she had missed hearing his voice, and the way he said her name, and how he told her he loved her. They were the feelings that made up part of her love for him. "Oh, Sam," she spoke into the darkness, "why can't I just say good-bye to you and mean it? Even though I can't make a decision, why am I so happy now?"

She looked at the clock and saw that only five minutes had elapsed since his call. She wondered how many times she would recreate their conversation before she fell asleep. She burrowed down under the blanket, once again remembering the operator's words: *"La Signorina Jarvis, per favore . . .* please."

Chapter Nineteen

It was difficult to keep her mind on her classes. Every day that she assigned homework, she would tick off the date in her head as though there were an invisible calendar inside her head. *Two more days until Sam comes. One more day until he comes.* She looked through the open window in her classroom and smelled the fragrance of the lilac bushes and apple trees in bloom. Yes, spring could be lovely too.

"Well, only two more months until vacation," Rene said as she came in. "Sometimes, Katie, I wish for something to look forward to." She swept back her dark hair. "Maybe I need something new and different in my life. Speaking of new things, have you figured out what to say to him?"

"No. Can you honestly see me running off to heaven knows where, living in a different country, not having a permanent home?"

"You don't have to. There are such things as coast-to-coast marriages. They're rather popular now."

Katie shook her head. "Not for me."

"Then come up with a better alternative. But don't be a fool. The Sam Hubbards of the world don't come along every day of your life. There aren't many guys who can put a sparkle in a woman's eyes like he has in yours. Think hard about it, Katie." She took out her car keys. "Are you coming?"

On their way to the parking lot, they passed the field where Jason was coaching the baseball team, and Katie stopped to watch him while Rene went on. He seemed to be taking the broken engagement quite well. Whenever they saw each other, they were still friendly, and, in fact, the rest of the faculty, with the exception of Rene, didn't even know that they were no longer planning their marriage. Now that she was no longer engaged to him, she could see that marriage would have been completely wrong for them. How could she have not seen it before? They were mismatched; the only thing they had in common was teaching, which was not enough to base a lifetime on.

When she waved to him, he motioned her to sit down on the sidelines. "I want to talk to you," he yelled, and then went back to the kids he was coaching. He picked up a bat to demonstrate a bunt. Then he gave it to the next hitter and walked over to her and tossed her a baseball.

"I've been wanting to talk to you," he said, sitting down beside her. "I've got some news, and I didn't want to tell it to anyone yet except you."

As she raised her eyebrows, Jason laughed. "No, don't worry, I'm not going to try to convince you to come back to me. I'm positive now that we really shouldn't be together."

She touched his arm. "We're not destined to be married to each other, but we'll always be good friends, won't we?"

"More than that, Katie. We're great friends." He tossed the baseball back and forth in his hands. "You know, after we first talked, when you told me about how you couldn't marry me, I thought about it for a long time. Sure, I was hurt."

"I tried not to . . ." she said gently.

"Oh, it wasn't your fault. You were saying things that I just didn't want to hear. I couldn't understand why we weren't suited to each other. And then I did. We sure did take each other for granted. I even took myself for granted." He laughed again, and she could see the gentle creases around his eyes. "I was boring, and I got accustomed to doing things the same old way all the time," he said. "And I was stuck in a dead-end job here, and it was as though I never kept up with what life had to offer." He rubbed the scuffed ball on his pants. "Oh, you never said that, but I'll tell you, Katie, when you left, I had to do a lot of soul-searching. About you, us, and me and my career. And I decided that maybe now was the time for me to move on, to start shifting gears, to enjoy life, to go after another job. And that's what I did. I applied for the position of assistant principal at Woodward High — and I got it."

His eyes were shining and his face was animated, and she was happy to see, for the first time since she had known him, that he was more than just content with himself and his profession. "They just called me to tell me I could have the job if I want it. So I took it. How's that for *carpe diem,* for seizing the day?"

"That's wonderful, really wonderful! I'm so happy for you. When do you start at Woodward?"

"In September. And maybe someday I'll come back here and be principal." He resumed tossing the ball. "How's that for thinking big?"

"Oh, Jason, you're really on your way! And I don't doubt you'll be principal here someday." She patted his arm. "What about baseball? I know you love it, that you love teaching the kids."

"You always did know me so well. Couldn't leave baseball, could I? I'll still be a coach. Woodward needs me — desperately! They've got a one and three record already." He tossed the ball into his mitt. "So it looks like I'll be moving on after this term. I just wanted you to be the first to know."

"Thanks," she said, touched that he had told her his news first. "I'll even come to see your team play."

He shook his head slowly. "I don't think so, Katie. You may not be around here."

She blinked at the truthfulness of the statement. "Maybe."

He looked at the players in the outfield and then stood up. "Gotta get back to the team. This may be my last winning season for a while."

"I doubt that," Katie said. "Great coaches make great teams."

He waved, then jogged back to his team. At least something good had come out of the broken engagement. Jason would be fine, just fine, now. It was a funny way to look at it, but Sam had given him a gift too.

Chapter Twenty

Katie drove home, not hearing the music on the radio, absorbed with the thought of Jason and his new position. It would be lonely for her at the school next semester. She would miss him.

She parked the car and went into her building, stopping off at the mailbox. No letter. Sam must have thought more about it, about coming to see her, and had decided against it. Perhaps she hadn't sounded encouraging enough. No, that was wrong; she knew it was only her imagination, making up all sorts of scenarios for her. In the past two weeks she had invented all kinds of reasons and excuses why he wasn't coming. He had thought about it and decided to stay away. He didn't love her. He thought she had changed her mind. No, she thought, pushing the elevator button, she had to stop telling herself all those horror stories. He had said he was coming and he was the type of person to keep his word.

She pushed the button again. *Oh, Sam,* she thought, *I wish I could tell you all that's been happening in my life. How I'm not going to marry Jason . . . how I've decided that I'm going to*

*go back next year and ski Devil's Mist . . .
how much I miss you.* She bit her lip. That
crazy feeling of finding excuses why Sam
hadn't arrived yet overtook her again. He
should have been here already. He just wasn't
coming — the words echoed and reverberated
through her head. *Well, no use crying about
something that's over,* she thought, wearily accepting the *fait accompli* of the imagined act.
She should have taken Rene's advice. She
should have followed her heart and told Sam
on the phone that she loved him and wanted
to see him again and again. She smiled at the
realization that she was changing, just as Jason
was changing. But as for leaving her job,
friends, and home for someone she hardly
knew — no, she couldn't be expected to do
that. But still. . . .

"I think you and I have a lot to talk about."

She heard the deep voice from behind her,
and she tensed at the words. It couldn't be
Sam . . . he was still overseas. She whirled
around toward the alcove with a chair and
a window overlooking the courtyard. He was
standing there with his coat over his shoulder
and his luggage on the floor. As the uneven
smile appeared on his face, she felt as though
her heart was too full . . . too fragile and near-
ing the breaking point.

"Sam," she murmured, drawing out the

word so that no others were necessary to tell him her feelings. She searched his face for the lines of laughter that she had noticed and liked immediately when she met him at Mountain Laurel. The creases were still there, but they were deeper now, and she wondered if they were caused by sadness.

She watched his eyes as they caressed her, and she swallowed hard as his hands reached out, first to touch her arm gently and then to pull her cautiously to him.

"Sam." She could only repeat his name, numbed by the surprise of seeing him. "Sam." She had wished for this for weeks, and now that he was here, all she could do was to stand helplessly, trying to think of the right words to say.

"I've been waiting for almost the whole afternoon," he said, and then opened the elevator door. "I even know where you live and who lives in the building." He smiled at her and she felt as though sunshine had flooded the lobby. "I've met the nicest people while waiting for you."

Inside the elevator, she could only shake her head and marvel at his being there, and continue to speak his name.

"Say something else," he urged. "Say something like, 'Sam, it's good to see you. I'm glad you're here.' Say anything."

"Sam, it's good to see you. I'm glad you're here," she said, and they both laughed. "I kept thinking that we hardly said anything on the phone."

"We said enough." He gestured her to precede him from the elevator. "I'm here, aren't I?"

"Yes," she said as they crossed the corridor to her door. "Come in."

He laughed the deep booming laugh she remembered from Mountain Laurel. "Katie-Katie, you don't think I came all the way here just to stand in halls, do you?" He closed the door behind him and looked at her. "You look great," he said, and she could only stand there mute, watching him, remembering his every gesture. This was what she had wanted since coming home, and now she was dumbstruck.

"Well," he said, putting his coat on the couch. "Aren't you going to say something?"

She took a deep breath. "You've sort of taken me by surprise. I didn't expect you."

"I told you I'd be here." He looked at her and suddenly his eyes clouded. "I couldn't forget you, Katie. And I didn't want to. It was as though a part of my life was left behind at Mountain Laurel, somewhere on the ski slopes, left there with the cold and the snow and the winter. I couldn't forget you, not in Italy or Switzerland or any of the other places where I was. Everything reminded me of you." He held up his hand to stop her from saying anything. "You and I have got to talk. We've got to come to some resolutions, and it has to be that we're going to be together, whether it's physically or emotionally, and no matter whether we're in the same place or not."

As he touched her shoulder and buried his head in her hair, she remembered once again the days and nights at the lodge. "I can't let you go, Katie-Katie," he said. "I think that it would be a terrible mistake for both of us."

"You get only one chance," she mumbled.

"What?"

"Someone once told me that you get only one really glorious chance at love."

"That's absolutely true." As he kissed her lips, she remembered the rushing of the wind on the mountain slopes.

"Sam."

"There you go again with my name." He kissed her once more and then guided her to the couch. "Talk to me, Katie. Tell me you love me, that we can work it out."

She swallowed hard so that her voice would be heard: "If I talk to you right this minute, then I'm not going to be able to think clearly and I'll agree to anything."

"Good." He took her hands. "Then it will

only take me a few minutes to convince you that we should just go ahead and get married."

She held up her hand. "Wait, Sam, wait. It's not that easy. There are problems. . . ."

He shook his head and kissed her again. "I don't see any."

"That's because you don't want to." He nuzzled her neck and she tried to move away. "Please don't. Let's talk."

"That's exactly what I've been trying to do." He grinned at her, and she saw the marvelous glow in his eyes and again she was reminded of the lodge.

"Oh, Sam. Don't do this to me." She got up and sat in the chair opposite him. "You're right, I do love you." She saw him smile at her. "You knew that, didn't you? You knew I fell in love with you almost right away." How could she help it, she thought, especially when he looked at her with the uneven smile that made her heart want to grow bigger so that she had more love to give him.

"And I love you." He held out his hands. "That's the only thing that matters," he said.

She looked around at the apartment. "But this is my life. I'm a teacher. I love my job. And I'm not as adventuresome as you. I told you that before."

He got up, walked around the room, and saw the photo of them. "I wondered if you ever looked at it," he said. He picked up the picture and then put it down again.

"Yes, of course I do."

"I love you, Katie." He said it again, and she felt powerless. "Marry me, Katie." Just the way he said it made her want to believe that everything could be worked out.

"I have a job that I like."

"You can keep it — or work in another place." He kissed her cheek. "Teachers are always needed."

"I don't really want to leave. This is my home."

"You don't have to — for now. But later, Katie, we can have all those things you want — the house . . . even the flowers in the garden, or a home in the mountains where we can ski anytime we want. Anything, Katie, anything you want." His lips moved to the tip of her nose and he kissed it and then continued on to her lips. "What else?"

"I want a husband to be here with me always."

He pulled his head back and looked at her with somber eyes. "That I can't promise, Katie. At least not for now."

"My mother and father. . . ." She looked up at the ceiling so that she wouldn't have to see his wonderful face, the face that could convince her to do almost anything.

"Maybe it was more than just the traveling. Maybe their love wasn't strong enough to survive the times they were apart." It was the same thing that Rene had said to her. "Ours *will* be." He looked at her with probing eyes. "Can't you make a few changes, Katie?"

"Some things — yes. But Sam, I don't want phone calls and postcards from every part of the world to remind me that I have a husband. I want *you*." Why not tell him the truth? She looked at him. He had come from so far to see her. Why couldn't there be a solution?

He paced the floor and then stopped. "It's all I can offer you right now, that and my love, my always faithful love no matter where I am." He picked up a music box. "Reminds me of when we met." She nodded and said nothing, distracted by the scattered tinkling from the box. She couldn't lose him now — now that she knew how much she loved him.

He resumed his pacing. Finally he stopped, sat down on the edge of the couch, and drummed his fingers on the arm. "Can't we both compromise?" he asked, and she watched him through misty eyes. "Suppose I ask for a transfer in about six months and then stay closer to home . . . maybe travel only on the East Coast, so that you can see me on weekends and some weekdays. . . ."

"And my birthdays?" she asked in a half

whisper, startled to realize that finally there could be agreement.

"And your birthdays and my birthdays." He stroked her hair, pushing it back from her face. "And maybe Washington's Birthday and Valentine's Day and all the other'important holidays." His fingers soothed her cheek and moved slowly across her face to her mouth until they covered her lips. "What would you say to that?" he asked her.

There was nothing for her to say. Instead, she kissed his fingers. Six months wouldn't be too long to wait. By then it would be time to return to Mountain Laurel.

"We can make it, Katie-Katie." He put his hands on her cheeks so that she had to look at him, and she saw that his eyes had become bright again. "Look at me, Katie," he said, and then laughed. "What you see is what you get."

"Oh, Sam!" she cried out, and then clung to him. He was the joy of her life . . . her one glorious love. Six months would be over quickly. She held him tightly and kissed him. Next year, she knew, she would conquer Devil's Mist. Next year she and Sam would ski the mountain . . . together.

The employees of THORNDIKE PRESS hope you have enjoyed this Large Print book. All our Large Print books are designed for easy reading — and they're made to last.

Other Thorndike Large Print books are available at your library, through selected bookstores, or directly from us. Suggestions for books you would like to see in Large Print are always welcome.

For more information about current and upcoming titles, please call or mail your name and address to:

THORNDIKE PRESS
PO Box 159
Thorndike, Maine 04986
800/223-6121
207/948-2962